The Smithsonian Institution from Pennsylvania Avenue and Eleventh Street, 1874.

Physically, these tightly-buttoned ladies and high-collared gentlemen belong to another age, but their spirit is timeless.

THE COSMOS CLUB ON LAFAYETTE
SQUARE, CIR. LATE 1880's.

HENRY ADAMS

SIMON NEWCOMB

JOHN WESLEY POWELL

HORATIO KING

EDWARD M. GALLAUDET

JOSEPH HENRY

CLARENCE E. DUTTON   ASAPH HALL

JOHN SHAW BILLINGS   SPENCER F. BAIRD

JOSEPH M. TONER

OTIS T. MASON

GARRICK MALLERY

CLARENCE KING

FRANK HAMILTON CUSHING

WILLIAM HENRY HOLMES

SIMON NEWCOMB (seated on stool) AT THE UNITED STATES
NAVAL OBSERVATORY, 1874.

W. J. McGEE   ANITA NEWCOMB McGEE

MATILDA COXE
STEVENSON

ALICE CUNNINGHAM
FLETCHER

GROVE K. GILBERT

LESTER FRANK WARD

JAMES C. WELLING

UNITED STATES GEOLOGICAL SURVEY FAREWELL DINNER
IN HONOR OF JOHN WESLEY POWELL.

(Powell in right foreground: W. J. McGee in left foreground.)

LIST OF PHOTOGRAPHS

DESIDERATUM
IN
WASHINGTON

DESIDERATUM IN WASHINGTON

The Intellectual Community
In the Capital City
1870-1900

by
J. KIRKPATRICK FLACK

FOR JAN

Preface

One hundred years ago Washington, D. C. seemed on the threshold of cultural greatness. With a purposeful body of local residents and public officials committed to making it the national center of science and scholarship, the city appeared close to becoming the intellectual as well as the political capital of the United States. This prospect had always facinated those who saw in such a combination of mind and power the key to the promise of American life. Since the early 1800's it had been felt that the seat of government should accomodate and support the nation's leading men of learning so that they might better serve their society. Yet this hope proved as frustrating as it was enchanting, and as the nineteenth century wore on the want of a distinct intellectual community could be considered the requisite factor missing from the development of the Federal City.

Then following the Civil War emerged a coherent body of scientists, educators, and literary personages. The group identity of these genteel individuals was established by the associations that they founded and actively participated in, and their self-image stemmed from an awareness of shared purposes. Here was the long desired element which would bring a leavening of capital society while it used its collective influence to promote national culture, particularly through public science. With this "desideratum" Washington's special destiny seemed assured.

To understand such glorious expectations, we must regard what was occuring in Washington as part of the overall context of cultural disruption. According to contemporaries, Washington, like the rest of the postbellum nation, suffered from a lack of essential order. Symptomatic of this condition were such well documented Gilded Age characteristics as an absence of taste and discrimination, lax standards of polite behavior, and the appalling frivolity of social intercourse. One antidote was the formation of genteel circles, coteries of fastidious men and women whose lofty amusements served as precepts for the society in general. Though these elegant groups never attained the intellectual distinction which they craved, their existence tended to improve the tone of life at the capital, and to a significant degree, their popularity added momentum to the drive for establishing serious-minded organizations.

The 1870's brought a noticeable increase in the number and vitality of local scientific societies. This phenomenon was pre-war in origin, but it drew strength from certain trends of late nineteenth century culture. Most important was the expansion of government science and the concomitant growth of Washington's scientific population. These individuals were inclined to be optimistic about the nation's future because of the strides being taken in their own disciplines; indeed they felt that the enhancement of the scientific estate would automatically bring cultural progress. First, however, it was necessary to organize Washington's scientists so as to give them professional standing and make them more effective.

The vogue of cultivated societies suggested how this might be accomplished. New intellectual groups would confer prestige on their members thereby making them socially attractive; situated in the nation's capital they would facilitate alliances with public officials whose backing was vital to national science; their resources could be used for stimulating popular interest; and professionally, they would increase and diffuse knowledge and strengthen ties between various groups of specialists. Thus the movement to create learned associations was multifaceted, and while its main impulse was scientific its general effect was much broader. Membership in organizations such as the Philosophical Society, the Cosmos Club, and the Washington Academy of Sciences was not confined to practitioners of science—the only requirement for admission was a firm commitment to advancing national culture.

The developmental process of the Washington intellectual community therefore reveals several sides of late nineteenth century America. In the first instance it shows that Gilded Age stereotypes hardly do justice to the complexity and creativity of this period. It also suggests that intellectuals were gaining informal representation in official Washington. Their response to unsettled conditions indicates how the search for order hastened the professionalization and institutionalization of intellectual life. The operations of Washington's societies demonstrates how the prevailing mode of organization was turned to account in promoting science. Finally, the history of the intellectual community illuminates the imperishable vision of a group of sensitive individuals who sought to understand and influence their own times. In the present volume I have attempted to explain the origins and early growth of this body, to elucidate its particular assumptions about cultural elitism, and to relate its internal history to the larger patterns of late nineteenth century social experience.

Because Washington's intellectual community had been considered but indirectly by previous historians, my investigation was made relatively easy. The paucity of scholarly accounts meant that I did not have to revise recognized schools of interpretation while formulating explanations of my own. Without a body of secondary literature to draw from, however, I had to rely considerably on the insights of persons who had speculated about the subject, and who were able to reveal obscure documents and otherwise help guide my research. Thus, it becomes a pleasant duty to acknowledge my indebtedness to the numerous individuals and institutions who facilitated this study.

Edward Lurie first suggested the topic when I was a beginning doctoral student in his American intellectual history seminar at Wayne State University. He continued to direct my work during the dissertation stage and subsequently proved instrumental in helping me prepare the manuscript for publication. Throughout this long process I have acquired an unbounded respect for his knowledge of the field, his high standards of craftsmanship, and, above all, his patience.

Many scholars gave me the benefit of stimulating criticism. I am deeply grateful for the abiding encouragement shown by friends and colleagues at the Smithsonian Institution and in the History Department of the University of Maryland. I should like to offer special thanks to certain persons who read various drafts, provided detailed suggestions, and generously shared their understanding of the subject: Hamilton Cravens, George Crossette, Constance McLaughlin Green, Curtis M. Hinsley, Paul H. Oehser, Nathan Reingold, and Wilcomb E. Washburn.

The staffs of those libraries and archives cited in the "Essay on Sources" went beyond mere courtesy in making accessible their research materials. In this regard, I enjoyed the extended cooperation of the Library of Congress and the libraries of the Smithsonian Institution. I also appreciate being graciously permitted to quote from manuscripts housed in the American Institute of Physics; the American Philosophical Society; the Biological Society of Washington; the John Hay Library, Brown University; the Chemical Society of Washington; the Burton Historical Collection, Detroit Public Library;the Geological Society of Washington; the Houghton Library, and the Museum of Comparative Zoology Library, Harvard University; the Rutherford B. Hayes Library; the Henry E. Huntington Library and Art Gallery; the Milton S. Eisenhower Library, The Johns Hopkins University; the Manuscript Division of the

Library of Congress; the Massachusetts Historical Society; the University of Michigan Library; the New-York Historical Society; the New York Public Library; the Arthur and Elizabeth Schlesinger Library on the History of Women in America, Radcliffe College; the National Anthropological Archives, and the Library of the National Collection of Fine Arts and the National Portrait Gallery, Smithsonian Institution; the Smithsonian Institution Archives; the Southwest Museum Library; and the Yale University Library.

Initial research was supported by a grant from the Society of Colonial Dames of America, administered through the History Department of Wayne State University. For this and other forms of assistance I would like to express my appreciation to Alfred H. Kelly. A predoctoral fellowship at the Smithsonian Institution afforded me a year of uninterrupted research and writing, as well as the means to travel to distant libraries. My project was aided further by a Faculty Research Award from the General Research Board of the Graduate School, University of Maryland. I also wish to thank Walter Rundell, Jr., chairman of the History Department, University of Maryland, who provided for the typing of the final manuscript.

LeRoy Bellamy, Nellie C. Carico, George Crossette, William Deiss, Chang-Su Houchins, George E. Hutchinson, Robert W. Rhynsburger, and Robert A. Truax helped me locate and identify pictorial evidence. Elizabeth White Beverly's steady competence in typing and mechanical matters was invaluable, as it has been to so many other frenzied authors. I am obliged to the publisher, and particularly to Michael Zambrelli for his painstaking editing of the manuscript.

Finally, my dedication reflects not gratitude for the customary collaboration of a mate, but rather my heartfelt awareness that without Jan LeMessurier Flack's devoted companionship this book could never have been written.

J. K. F.

Washington, D.C.

"I congratulate you on the establishment of the Cosmos—such a meeting place must have long been a desideratum in Washington—won't you tell me where it is?"

Edward Bigmore to T. F. Dwight
(February 25, 1879)

CONTENTS

Chapter

1

Flabby, Shambling Times

In the spring of 1973 the members of Washington's Cosmos Club were told that, "One of our current problems is a fear amoung the alleged intelligentsia of establishing an élite." The speaker was Louis Booker Wright, historian, librarian, and man of letters. He had just been presented with the Club's tenth annual award for distinguished service in advancing science, literature, and the arts. His speech was an appeal to genuine intellectuals to assert themselves in the direction of national culture. It was a familiar plea. Eight years earlier Henry Allen Moe, secretary-general of the Guggenheim Foundation, had taken a similar opportunity to sound the call for "an aristocracy of brains and character, an aristocracy with a conscience and a sense of history." Carefully ruling out aristocracies grounded on anything but intellect, Moe explained the pressing need to tap the well-springs of genius, to identify intellectuals who both dreamed and schemed, and to organize such men of knowledge and dedication so that they could help fulfill the promise of American life. "Without an aristocracy, we should be lost; having it, we surely shall be saved."[1]

These words, spoken in 1965 and again in 1973, could not have been more appropriately chosen. They echoed exactly the sentiments of Henry Adams, a founder of the Club and one of its premier members. In 1862 he had written to his older brother, Charles Francis, Jr.:

> We want a national set of young men like ourselves or better, to start new influences not only in politics, but in literature, in law, in society, and throughout the whole social organism of the country—a national school of our own generation.[2]

The message of Moe and Wright, therefore, harkened back to the inexorable purpose of the Cosmos Club as a self-selected embodiment of wisdom and goodness, an elitist institution in a democratic society.

This purpose stands in strange contrast to the tenor of today. Moe, Wright, and Adams could consider a world undistinguished for intellectual leadership and direction deleterious. In our own time, however, the very nature of intellectual elitism in government, in universities, in mass communications, and in cultural decision making is thought to hasten the ruination of contemporary society. Ironically, the impulse to redeem and restore America is held responsible for turning America into a moral monster. With the moral elite greatly separated from the large mass of the population, it now becomes clear that the Adamses, the Moes, and the Wrights created for themselves a world of eternal frustration by building upon an almost impossible base: the attempted congruence of democratic ideals with elitist drives and purposes.

The establishment of the Cosmos Club represented an effort to draw together men of scientific, scholarly, and educational merit for purposes of creating a milieu favorable to its members' work, while at the same time adding to their collective prestige and influence. Membership constituted an acknowledged badge of honor. Those chosen for the Club were held in high esteem. Not so high, perhaps, as those in Gondour, Mark Twain's fictitious republic wherein social rank and voting power increased proportionately to one's wealth and education. Intellectuals in Gondour dominated the government, and there were few more exalted citizens than the country's leading astronomer, to whom one and all doffed their hats and bowed deeply in deference to his scholarly distinction.[3] American scientists, however, hardly enjoyed such obeisance, as Simon Newcomb, an eminent astronomer and early member of the Cosmos Club, pointed out.[4]

Despite such complaints, during the latter part of the nineteenth century the respect and recognition accorded Washington's men of parts greatly increased, a phenomenon which coincided with the birth of associations informing the Capital City's intellectual establishment. Institutions such as the Cosmos Club had a direct bearing upon the organization of an intellectual elite. Furthermore, they had a salutary affect on society in general. Besides enhancing the position of intellectuals, they brought a measure of tone and purpose to what an astute contemporary termed "flabby, shambling times."[5]

Such epithets traditionally serve to characterize the lack of form in American culture after the Civil War. New wealth, born of an industrial system which was rapidly maturing and expanding, challenged the leadership of an older established class. This was axiomatic in a land where "success" meant material accomplishment, and where instant prestige went hand-in-hand with sudden wealth. Social prominence was the deserved reward for those who had gotten ahead in the economic struggle. In an increasingly fluid social order there were abundant examples of a rapid ascent from obscurity to distinction. In the 1870's, as before, vertical mobility was celebrated as a positive aspect of national character, something which lay at the very heart of the democratic faith. Was not the *arriviste* living proof that the doctrine of free opportunity for all really worked?

The question scarcely required an answer; yet the swift rise of large numbers of parvenus did not win universal acclaim. Rapid mobility produced social instability, and those whose positions were disturbed reproached the new men for not having paused to cultivate characteristics which distinguished an American aristocrat. Such attributes as appreciation for scholarship, recognition of aesthetic excellence, worthwhile conversation, avoidance of opulent display, and a sense of public service—traits which might be acquired without breeding— seemed in short supply among the *nouveaux riches*. Perhaps the tenets of good manners and good form had not been considered all that seriously by previous generations. Nevertheless, when they were found lacking in the upstarts these standards were enshrined as absolute virtues, and those who failed to meet them were derided as "the aristocracy of shoddy."[6]

The elevation of new wealth was not in itself cause for concern. The sheer swiftness with which this new class asserted itself was not the principal irritant. "The suddenly rich are on a level with any of us nowadays," proclaimed the Brahmin father to his son in *The Rise of Silas Lapham.*

> . . . there's no doubt but money is to the fore now. It is the romance, the poetry of our age. It's the thing that chiefly strikes the imagination. The Englishmen who come here are more curious about the great new millionaires than about anyone else, and they respect them more. It's all very well. I don't complain of it.[7]

Charles Francis Adams, Jr., a real-life Brahmin with one foot firmly planted in the world of commerce and finance, sounded the same note: "They may say what they please, but today wealth is the [leverage ground] in America . . . I want wealth as the springboard to influence, consideration, power, and enjoyment." In 1887 he admitted that "I have all I want—and I want a great deal." [8] Obviously, not all men of genteel background found *nouveau* values repugnant. What caused consternation, however, was the disregard exhibited by the new class for social bearing.

There was slight awareness among the newly rich, of the obligations of patrician leadership, of the responsibility for setting criteria of behavior and discrimination. Indeed, they were as vulgar as the society that had provided them with the means and opportunities for their new status. Their personal shallowness was looked upon as symptomatic of the general low level of national culture. Critics were contemptuous of both.

Charles Eliot Norton, from the vantage point of the chair of fine arts at Harvard, pronounced his verdict on post-bellum America: "This generation is given over to the making and spending of money, and is losing the capacity of thought."[9] He looked about him and concluded that his countrymen lavished every ounce of their mental energies on material pursuits. Because they could think of nothing else, intellectual life in America was fast dying-out. Norton felt that there had not been, to begin with, much congeniality toward the creative spirit. Like Clarence King, he believed that Americans were simply "an unartistic people, with neither an indigenous nor an adopted art language in which to render grand thoughts. We are ignorant of the meaning and use of *style* . . . ."[10] His own generation of philistines outdid others in insensibility toward everything but material abundance and petty amusements. He constantly brooded over the moral and intellectual degeneracy which, he insisted, resulted from the high social premium placed upon affluence.

> Wealth has become the chief modern form of power, and, usurping the dominion of the old ideals over the imagination, it is sought, not only as a means to other ends, but as itself an end. And it has a great advantage over other objects of desire, in its capacity of securing general and immediate recognition, and in its power to inflame the dullest intelligence by its direct appeal to the sensibilities of men.

He decried the "lack of intellectual elevation and of moral discrimination" as a source of national weakness; "The prevalence of vulgarity" he viewed as a "national disgrace."[11] Search as he might it was impossible for him to discern the faintest glimmer of aesthetic or social achievement.

Norton's attitude toward American life was not always laden with gloom. Before the Civil War he was optimistic about the portents for national improvement. "The grandeur of our opportunities is proportional to the immensities of our deficiencies," he wrote in 1857, "so that one may rejoice to be an American even while seeing how far we fall short in many ways of what is accomplished elsewhere."[12] During the sectional struggle he watched the North grow more enlightened and become infused with idealism. Like his Cambridge neighbor, Louis Agassiz, he felt that through the war effort "slumbering citizens had been aroused and the nation 'manured' to bring forth a glorious harvest."[13]

To insure that succeeding harvests would be equally rewarding, Norton helped found the *Nation,* a genteel magazine designed to broadcast patriotic sentiments and nourish a feeling of national commitment and cohesion. He might not have gone as far as J. W. DeForest's Dr. Ravenel, who was made to assert that "In these days—the days of Lincoln, Grant, and Sherman—faith in the imagination—faith in the supernatural origins of humanity—becomes possible," but certainly Norton anticipated that 1860's would be remembered as an epoch of moral purpose, and that this spirit was bound to regenerate American democracy and culture.[14]

Not many years later he was thoroughly disillusioned. The experience of sacrifice had failed to usher in a heroic age; rather the war gave way to a period of sterility made more tragic by the hopefulness of the bygone era. As the decade of the sixties ended he engaged in an agonizing reappraisal of America's present condition and outlook for the future. Not surprisingly, for this was true of the Brahmin stripe, sometime around 1870 Norton lost faith in the promise of America. Recurring illness, personal bereavement, the degradation of Grant's second term in office, and the tearing down of "walls dear to Norton's memory" combined to undermine his optimism.[15] In 1873, two years after his wife's death, Norton lamented that "all life is likely to be solitary in America to one who cannot share that confident spirit of cheerful optimistic fatalism..."[16] He would have applauded Walt Whitman's observation: "It is as if we were somehow being endowed with a vast and more and more thoroughly appointed body, and then left with little or no soul."[17]

To men who believed deeply that the nation was destined for some sort of spiritual greatness, post-war America seemed depressingly hollow and superficial. In a society of "small aims, or no aims at all," said Whitman, it was not the poet and the statesman who were admired, but rather the "fashionably dressed speculators and vulgarians." The Gilded Age was worse than a comedy of manners; that it was wretched in the extreme, was the consensus among the social types that historians have defined as "The Best Men," "the cosmopolitan gentry," and the guardians of the genteel tradition.[18] "I came here fifty years ago with high and fond ideals about America," recalled E. L. Godkin, editor of the *Nation.* "They are now all shattered, and I apparently have to look elsewhere to keep even moderate hopes about the human race alive."[19] The same tone of resounding bitter-

ness was struck in an 1878 letter of Dr. Joseph T. Webb, Rutherford
Hayes's brother-in-law, as he replied to an invitation to a veteran's gathering of the 23rd Ohio Volunteers: "You ask if I shall attend the reunion . . .
I shall not . . . it was the mistake of my life in joining the Reg't. I sacrificed
my business, and all for what?"[20]

Three quarters of a century earlier John Adams visualized for America
a coming period of high cultural attainment, a period during which the
gentleman-scholar could devote himself to a life of art, to activities of the
mind and spirit. But the Gilded Age realities made a mockery of Adams's
ideal. Rather than having as its hallmark a natural aristocracy of worth,
the post-bellum decades were stamped with a plutocratic element whose
chief merit was the ability to accumulate wealth. The age was characterized by individuals like Christopher Newman, Henry James's representative American in the post-war era, who believed that substantial railroad
investments served as a free pass into the best social circles.[21] Such men
were both pretentious and extravagant. They used palatial mansions, sea-
shore summer homes, immoderate entertainment, and international mar-
riages to cloak their humble origins. Congressman "Sunset" Cox, of New
York, summed up the condition during his campaign of 1872 as "an insane
greed for wealth . . . the desire to shine in the calcium glare of the present
feverish round of social and political junketing."[22] As the century passed
into its final quarter, Godkin judged that the seventies were "filled with
more social garishness and bad taste than any other decade in American
history."[23]

The Gilded Age was hardly the first period to hear cries of anguish
about the upsurge of materialism and the degradation of national character. In one version or another, the jeremiad has been a continuing refrain
from the New England Puritans to the New York intellectuals. As an
atavistic impulse it is especially pronounced during times of rapid social
change. Puritanism itself can be interpreted as a particular response to
social instability and personal anxiety, as "a way of organizing men to
overcome the acute sense of chaos."[24] Seventeenth century Massachusetts Bay settlers received eloquent injunctions against the pitfalls of
"worldliness," and stern warnings not to let prosperity get the better of
piety.[25] The dour concern with the social consequences of money-getting,
so rampant in the late nineteenth century, was also very much an antebellum phenomenon.

"New modes of reasoning and acting," the side-effects of New
England's progress, caused apprehension in the 1820's.[26] In 1836, the
New York State Medical Society reported that:

> The population of the United States is beyond that of other countires an anxious one. All classes are either striving for wealth, or endeavoring to keep up its appearance. . . . From these causes, and perhaps from the nature of our political institutions, and the effects arising from them, we are an anxious, care-worn people.[27]

"Nothing was settled," wrote Joseph G. Baldwin in 1853. "Chaos had come again, or rather, had never gone away."[28]

Equally familiar were the complaints that boorish men of wealth were robbing America of aesthetic appreciation. "I am out of place," Thomas Cole noted ruefully in 1838, "there are few persons of real taste; and no opportunity for the true artist to develop his powers."[29] Abram Hewitt did not have to wait until after the Civil War to assert that, "The consumption of iron is the social barometer by which to estimate the relative height of civilization among nations."[30]

Throughout the first half of the nineteenth century cultural spokesmen fretted over the corrosion of traditional ideals, while yearning wistfully for elegance and orderliness.[31] Yet, in spite of Emerson's reassurance that "every age, like every human body, has its own distemper,"[32] the obsession with material gain seemed almost pathological after the Civil War. As Mark Twain said of Jay Gould and his generation: "The people had *desired* money before his day, but *he* taught them to fall down and worship it."[33] Coupled with the widespread feeling that the times were out of joint, it appeared that post-war culture was doomed.[34]

In 1873 Francis Amasa Walker, professor of political economy at Yale's Sheffield Scientific School and superintendent of the United States Census, too gave vent to his apprehensions about Gilded Age America. What troubled him was that between 1860 and 1870 there was a diminution in the geometrically predicted rate of population increase.

He attributed the decline to the decadence which permeated American society. Throughout the antebellum period statisticians affirmed that an unbroken rise in future population was no less inevitable than uninterrupted national progress, and when it came to making a forecast for the sixties James D. B. DeBow, who in 1850 had headed the seventh census, confidently proclaimed that twenty years hence there would be almost forty-three million Americans. As it turned out Mr. DeBow over estimated by more than four and a quarter million, an astonishing miscalculation considering the accuracy of extrapolations for the earlier decades. Walker interpreted this failure to realize the projected gain as a sign of national malaise. According to his diagnosis there was every indication that the condition would grow worse, and very little reason to hope that it would get better.

If retardation could have been written off as a consequence of the Civil War, Walker reasoned, then there would be little cause for concern. Obviously this was an unnatural condition not likely to occur soon again; following a brief delay the curve of population could be expected to resume its steady ascent. But after totaling up the numerical loss due to military casualties, a temporary reduction in the birth rate, and the war's effects on immigration and former slaves, the aggregate was not nearly enough to account for the disappointingly low population figure for 1870. Thus Walker showed statistically that the war was not responsible for what had taken place and what seemed to lie ahead. Instead the decline had to be attributed to a combination of "social forces and tendencies, not heretofore felt, or at least not heretofore recognized, in our national life, [that] are beginning to affect powerfully the reproductive capabilities of our people."[35]

Walker's speculations about the enervating influences of mass society were apparently substantiated a few years later by the work of Dr. George Miller Beard, a New York City neurologist, who, in 1881, published the sensational book *American Nervousness*. Post-war Americans suffered from nervous exhaustion, he affirmed, because the unsettling forces of modern civilization caused a depletion of "nerve force." Although the symptoms identified by the doctor (insomnia, sweating hands and feet, involuntary emissions, dryness of the hair, fear of everything) were less acute than those noted by the professor, they both arrived at the same conclusion. For his part Walker wrote with considerable wit and many of his arguments were made tongue in cheek. Yet he appears to have been gravely earnest about this: "These forces and tendencies have contributed in a very large degree within the last decade to bring down the ratio of increase in the native population"[36]

What were these factors which Walker considered so deleterious? They were the by-products of mid-nineteenth century industrialization, the moral and social changes that ate away at traditional values underpinning American culture. The price of economic and urban growth was a weakening of the national character, and this was reflected in the census results. Where earlier statisticians had gone wrong, he argued, was in aligning themselves with the prophets of progress by considering material advancement conducive to population increase. Rather it was the other way around, that the rate of population declined in proportion to industrialization and urbanization because these processes had side effects which proved debilitating to the spirit. Since Americans showed no inclination to curb their appetites for the fruits of material development, Walker was pessimistic about the future.

> . . . as the whole population tends increasingly to fashion and social observance; as diet, dress, and equipage become more and more artificial; and as the detestable American vice of "boarding," making children truly "encumbrances," and uprooting the ancient and honored institutions of the family, extends from city to city and from village to village,—it is not to be doubted that we shall note a steady decline in the rate of the national increase from decade to decade.[37]

Though this dire forecast lacks Walker's customary precision, and even after making allowances for the fact that he sometimes was carried to extremes in pleading the importance of character,[38] his expressions of anxiety about post-war culture are highly revealing.

Walker went beyond bewailing the diminution of rectitude by locating the causes of this phenomenon in the "eddy and swirl of social and industrial currents through which the nation is now passing."[39] In other words, his pessimism was a response to cultural disorder and instability. He called attention to the fragmentation of American life, to the breakdown of traditional patterns of thought and behavior, and to the rupture of whatever cultural unity the country had possessed because he reckoned that here could be found the explanation for the distintegration of values. National character had waned, then, due to the absence of order following the Civil War. Indeed the disruption of culture was so complete that after the smoke of battle had cleared America seemed to be a different nation.

Henry Adams confessed that when part of his family returned to the United States from England in 1868, having missed observing the war at first hand, they were bewildered by the hasty transformation it had wrought and could not help feeling alienated from the new style of their native land.

> Had they been Tyrian traders of the year B. C. 1000, landing from a galley fresh from Gibralter, they could hardly have been stranger on the shore of a world, so changed from what it had been ten years before . . . . How much its character had changed or was changing, they could not wholly know, and they could but partly feel.[40]

The fabric of American civilization was unraveling, and in the process gentlemen such as Adams lost their traditional claims to positions of influence. They were resented because of their arrogance and ridiculed as being too precious, for querulously harping about decorum and propriety when what the country really cared for were steel rails and iron ingots. In contrast to the robber barons, who exuded machismo, they appeared socially impotent: "the gelded men of the Gilded Age." Eventually some of these individuals were able to reassert themselves by creating and taking advantage of new conduits to influence, but for the time being the impact of the Civil War upon Adams's class was devastating.[41] Nearly twenty years after the war ended, Charles Francis Adams, Jr. still talked anxiously about its unsettling effects, and feared that the nation's recovery demanded "quiet more than anything."[42]

For those who regarded continuity and equilibrium as fundamental precepts there seemed no escape from the prevailing condition of chaos, and the word anarchy came easily to their lips. "I was at Washington last week and found anarchy ruling our nation," wrote Henry Adams to Norton in 1871. "I don't know who has power or is responsible, but whoever it is, I cannot find him . . . ."[43] This confirmed his father's predictions that anarchy was not far off,[44] a prophesy that seemed fulfilled by the early seventies.

Against the background of economic depression which descended over the land in 1873—while Charles Eliot Norton continued to mourn the passing of idealism and intellectual vitality which he felt was a prelude to degeneracy, Francis Amasa Walker resumed the statistical analyses which seemed to confirm his worst fears about America's future, and Henry Adams proceeded with the excursions in scientific history which led him to conclude that the world was being drawn inexorably and with increasing rapidity toward annihilation[45] —President Grant began his second term in office and the grotesque spectacle of the Gilded Age lumbered on.

Many of the characteristics of this America could be discerned in Washington. Indeed, the city presented a mirror image of national culture: fortunes were quickly gained and the status of different social groups rapidly changed. The effects of these transformations were as visible in the Capital as in the nation at large.[46] "Wealth is omnipresent," wrote newspaperman Don Piatt, "and the humanities drive about in gorgeous carriages and live among stunning upholstery."[47] Parvenus competed with established families. Coarse showiness was manifest everywhere. It could be seen, for example, in the contrasting architectural styles of the Capital City. Elaborate ornamentation was juxtaposed to the simplicity and restraint of older buildings.

In 1874 newly planted trees symbolized a wealthy class which had not yet established its roots, and dusty, unpaved streets were emblematic of this group's unfinished character. "Much that was old," recalled one Washingtonian, "and part of it singularly delightful, had been destroyed. Most of that which was new was not only raw but in need of growth as well as refinement."[48] Newness and imperfection in a physical sense had their counterparts in Washington society.

There were elements of affluence as well as sham in the nabobs' manner of entertaining. Frank G. Carpenter ("Carp"), correspondent for the Cleveland *Leader,* and later a member of the Cosmos Club, reported that "the dinners of Washington could not be more expensive if their pepper and salt were grains of gold dust." Yet he detected a good deal of counterfeit.

> It is well known that Washington hostesses hire the china for their large balls and receptions. Almost every china store in this town has stocks of plain white dishes which go out and come back many times during the social season. I asked one of these merchants why the dishes used for this purpose were so plain. "It is not because people like them," he explained, "but because their guests cannot so easily tell that this is the same china they ate from the day before at another house."[49]

It was rumored too that the fine ladies of Washington rented their jewelry.

Some observers denied that Washington had any elegance whatsoever, and upbraided life at the Capital as an existence of "veneered furniture, plated spoons" and a place where "vulgar people who amass fortunes by successful gambling in stocks, pork, or grain can attain a great deal of cheap newspaper notoriety for their social expenditures . . . ."[50] Jane W. Gemmill, writing for the benefit of those who could not visit the Capital and view conditions for themselves, noted that "society, as at present existing in Washington, is very peculiarly made up, and at its best very hollow and unsatisfactory."[51] This criticism was mild compared with an account that stressed the meretricious rather than the artificial.

> There are more of the demimonde in Washington now than ever before. No law is put into force to stop them. They parade Pennsylvania Avenue in scores every bright afternoon, dressed in their sealskins and silks, either walking or driving in some of the best-looking turnouts in the city. They even enter the galleries of Congress...the private galleries reserved for the

members' families, where a member of Congress must have furnished the ticket for their admission.[52]

Placed in proper perspective Washington's seamy side could be taken as evidence of maturity; moral delinquency is often a natural part of the process of urbanization. But that was not the contemporary interpretation. Instead, there were exaggerated descriptions of raffishness, implications that the city reveled in sin, and was hopelessly debauched.

"Carp" described behavior that could be defined as nothing but bizarre.

> A curious feature of the wining and dining of Washington is the craze for giving entertainments of special colors. Not long ago Miss Bacon, the daughter of Representative Bacon of New York, gave a red luncheon at which the shades of the candles and glass globes were red, the bread and baked potatoes were tied with red ribbon, and a cushion of red tulips formed the centerpiece. The souvenirs were Japanese bonbons with dwarf red roses springing from their tops. Even the ice cream was red, in the form of strawberries in little red candy hampers.[53]

Whether focusing on moral shoddiness or simply aberrant conduct, what passed for society in Washington could be dismissed as nothing more than an unsavory spectacle. "Washington stood outside the social pale," said Henry Adams."No Bostonian had ever gone there."[54] His dismal opinion was confirmed by another contemporary who stated frankly that "the city does not offer many attractions to a stranger, and few care to remain after seeing the National Property."[55]

"Rents are high, food is bad, the dust is disgusting, the mud is deep, and the morals are deplorable," lamented a newspaper editor.[56] He was not alone in judging Washington totally unbearable. Frequently this condition was attributed to the nature of the population. In the spring of 1861 occurred an exodus of southerners who had been the stage managers of social life at the Capital throughout its history. Filling the vacuum was a hodgepodge of "politicians of every grade, adventurers of either sex, inventors of all sorts of military appliances, and simple citizens, good and bad."[57] Washington was without a class which could take the lead as a refining element in regard to tastes and habits. Other cities were more fortunate, and seemed to enjoy loftier amusements which brought about mental improvement and noble pursuits. But Washington was characterized by a "demoralizing haste to be rich, a vulgar, consuming passion for display."[58]

Members of the government, especially senators, set the tone. Their quarters tended to be sumptuous, and they entertained with "everything to eat and drink that money could buy."[59] Indeed, during the late sixties, what was reputed to be the most elegant house in Washington was owned by the millionarie senator from New York, Edwin D. Morgan.[60] Abigail Dodge, a cousin of the wife of James G. Blaine, who lived with the Blaine's in Washington, expressed the dominant view:

> Ill-gotten and well-gotten wealth have usurped the leadership of society. It is the custom, we are informed, for a society woman to dazzle, not by her beauty or conversation, but by the quality of her dress and the value of her jewels, and that a costume is not remarked upon as being in good taste and becoming, but as having cost so many hundred dollars.[61]

Brocade and bank notes were commonly employed to disguise fundamental social deficiencies; appurtenances of elegance passed for the real thing. "When you become conversant with our political society, you will find, with all its charmingness and brightness, that there are no convictions beneath it."[62] It must have been exceptional for one like Madeleine Lee, in Henry Adams's novel *Democracy,* who "was sober in her tastes" and "made no display," to create the impression of "luxury." Her sister, Miss Sybil Ross, was more typical. She had Paris dresses and "wore them and her ornaments according to all the formulas." But like the society she represented, "Sybil was transparent."[63]

Extravagance was most conspicuous in White House social functions. Dominated by elaborate, crowded receptions, such *tableaux vivants* struck Henry Adams as the "droll aping of monarchial forms." Formal dinners were excessively splendorous. During the Grant administration these assemblages were held regularly on Wednesday evenings, and stood as the high points of the "fashionable season." An average of thirty-six guests were seated in the state dining room, "suggestive of a baronial hall." Festoons and gilt vases were everywhere. The table was adorned with a long mirror, "a rare work of art" which would have permitted the diners to view themselves eating except for the columns of ferns which formed its border. The Italian steward, Melah, served twenty-nine courses. Six wine glasses were set before each plate and a new wine served with every third course.[64]

Few events equaled the wedding of the president's eighteen year old daughter in the executive mansion. Nellie Grant was a high spirited youth whose escapades caused much tongue-clucking among proper Washingtonians. They frowned on an upbringing which failed to "shield her from the allurements of pleasure," and shook their heads in dismay when she "suddenly 'came out' a fullfledged young woman of fashion, spoken of almost exclusively as the driver of a phaeton, and the leader of the all-night German."[65] Although her engagement to Algernon Sartoris, an English gentleman, was roundly disapproved of, they were married in May 1874, in what was reputed to be "the most elaborate wedding that ever took place in the White House."[66] The Marine Band played while guests were escorted into the East Room, where flowers bedecked the windows, walls, mantles, tables, chandeliers, and doorways. "The bride had a trousseau fit for an emperor's daughter, and the gifts showered upon her represented a fortune." [67] After the ceremony there was a breakfast followed by an inspection of presents: a dessert set of eighty-four pieces, a dinner service valued at $4,500, two rings, and emerald and a diamond, worth $1,000 each, a $500 handkerchief, and a $10,000 check from the father of the bride. "All the gifts were arranged by a special agent from Philadelphia, who attractively classified them in accordance with the stores from which they were purchased!" [68] A month later the president paid $3,827 in department store and dressmakers' bills, an amount that covered only New York and Philadelphia stores. The doubling of his salary in 1873 came none too soon!

Equally imperative was the establishment of rules of etiquette. Since elegant society entailed appropriate conventions of behavior this became a matter of first importance. Many families which were rapidly achieving notoriety were unaccustomed to observing proper courtesies, and much of Washington society was loud and uncouth. For the sake of order, and to reduce boorishness and confusion, it seemed wise to teach the social climbers accepted modes of conduct.

One who eagerly met this pedagogical challenge was Madeleine Vinton Dahlgren, a celebrated Washingtonian whose father had served twenty years in congress and whose late husband, Rear Admiral John A. Dahlgren, became widely known through his contributions to the U. S. Coast Survey and his seminal work in naval ordnance. Mrs. Dahlgren won fame on her own as an organizer of charitable activities, as an author and dominant force in Washington's Literary Society, and, most of all, as the self-appointed arbiter of taste. She was remarkably similar to the fictional heroine, Madeleine Lee: both were strong-willed and high-minded; both had lost distinguished husbands while they themselves were still in the prime of life; each engaged in philanthropy but restlessly sought more satisfying outlets for their reformist drives; ultimately, after shedding their widow's weeds, both tried to bring about a refinement of Washington society.[69] Mrs. Lee operated quietly, by turning her parlor into an exclusive salon for witty and clever people. Mrs. Dahlgren, on the other hand, was far more obtrusive. Her crusade took the form of a promulgation of ordinances for proper behavior, *Etiquette of Social Life in Washington,* which first appeared in 1873, went through many editions, and upset many people. A hostile clique developed in the Literary Society and Lucretia Garfield defied Mrs. Dahlgren by refusing to adopt her rigorous format for White House receptions.[70] Nonetheless, Madeleine Dahlgren remained a prominent figure in fashionable circles, as her "personal social register" clearly indicates. The rules which she laid down continued to be obeyed. There seemed to be general agreement about the urgent need for social guidelines.[71]

A spate of publications designed to serve as manuals of good manners appeared. They expounded intricate codes of conduct and prepared the reader for every conceivable situation.[72] Detailed directions fortified him against a myriad of possible *faux pas.* When to bow, how to shake hands, the writing of acceptances and regrets, dress, conversation, deportment at table—none of these were overlooked. But the primers on etiquette also aimed at a higher objective.

While providing for ordinary day-to-day contacts they sought to reconcile aristocratic customs with a non-aristocratic social order, or in other words, to "level-up democracy."[73] The desire for genteel appearances was writ large without denying the mythology of egalitarianism and classlessness. Adams's remark about the "aping of monarchial forms" contained more truth than humor. "Because we are a republic," proclaimed Mrs. Dahlgren, "we are not necessarily to be deprived of those amenities which render life agreeable."[74]

At the very least it should be understood that "though democracies may be rude they must not be inhospitable."[75] Refined forms and practices were not alien to the American environment. On the contrary, they were as indigenous as the founding fathers. Unfortunately, they had been dissipated earlier in the century by the waves of democratization. The alchemy of time made it appear that there had been a "rigid observance" of social etiquette in Washington's day. That golden age had endured the "radical sentiments" of Jefferson. "But General Jackson, when he became president, first broke down the barriers of careful respect. . . ."[76] Now they had to be reconstructed.

Most striking about this hand-wringing and beard-pulling, was the widespread concern with a lack of form and direction in Gilded Age America. The fact that a great many people were aware of the unsettled pattern of post-war life is significant. The war effort had evoked a spirit of national purpose, but it had not yielded the creation of a permanent cultural unity or identity. Fragmentation caused those who longed for cohesion to despair for the nation and its future. Social and economic changes rooted in the antebellum era and accelerated by the war itself had left American culture formless. To young George Santayana "society seemed to lack contrast and definition, as if everything were half formed and groping after its essence."[77]

The most obvious manifestation of this unformed condition was the indefinite status of taste and manners. If there had ever existed well rooted precedents for the conduct of social intercourse they had been buried in the avalanche of changes. Thus the urgency for new norms that would properly fit the post-war nation. Grant's fumbling attempts to establish practices for state functions illustrate this situation. The White House dinner parties and formal receptions reveal more than freakish behavior; they convey a sense of groping uncertainty as to how the president's social and ceremonial duties should be performed in the new era. Similarly, Grant's table setting is significant not as an example of grotesqueness, but because it bespeaks the "unbashed experimentation" that was so characteristic of the age.[78] Here was one dimension of the larger problem of cultural disorderliness. The drive for social conventions which could act as guides to proper conduct was therefore aimed at ameliorationg the general confusion about what constituted acceptable deportment.

Yet the confusion about polite courtesies was only the visible cap of the iceberg, nothing more than the most prominent features of disorder. The real dynamics of the Gilded Age were more complex than the commotion over which fork to use when. Such trifles merely called attention to the more fundamental disarrray of a disintegrated culture.[79]

Washington a century ago may not have been the majestic city that had long been envisioned, but neither was it a backwater village. Capital life was often praised by many people for its substance and its quiet dignity. "The society circle in Washington in 1873," recalled one observer, "was small compared with that of today. . . . The old Washingtonians were more *en evidence* than now and the political element came and went without disturbing in any marked degree the harmony of the social atmosphere."[80] "The circle in Washington was very small . . . and the entertainments many but simple."[81] Another resident wrote that it was "unnecessary for anyone to live beyond his position or to try to dazzle his neighbors by a too lavish parade of wealth."[82] In January, 1882, Henry James visited Washington for the first time:

I shouldn't wonder if the place were the most agreeable of our cities. The Henry Adamses, who are my principal friends here, have a commodious and genial house and have been very kind to me. The pleasant thing here is the absence of business—the economy-empty streets, most of them rather pretty, with nothing going on in them.[83]

Some people did enjoy an unhurried existence that was rich in its modesty. For those whose tastes were not pretentious, social intercourse could be consummately pleasant. In 1928, General Walker reminisced about Washington fifty years before:

[It was then] a delightful and hospitable town; there were no rich people; everybody had his daily work in some department of the government and carried his lunch with him—the most aristocratic in cotton napkins, the bourgeoisie in paper napkins. All went home to a half-past five o'clock dinner. For six months of the year the social life of Washington was on the front doorsteps of democratic, but none the less hospitable homes.[84]

Mrs. William Howard Taft maintained that the pernicious influence of new wealth was not felt until the close of the century.

In 1890 society in Wahington still consisted, chiefly, of the "best families" of the old city, the diplomatic corps and the highest among the government officials. A dinner party of twelve was still considered large, and only a few people had weekly evenings at home. There were occasional big receptions, but for nobody was society the mad rush that it is today. We ourselves lived very simply even for those simple days.[85]

During the Cleveland era, it could be said by a Smithsonian regent and member of the government, that "there are many pleasant things about the social side of public life in Washington. It is very democratic and yet one cannot go to a large dinner without meeting somebody well worth meeting. [86] As late as 1900 Washington was compared to "a village, where everyone knows everybody else;" where "the general air of its inhabitants is one of dignified ease;" where the citizenry was not "degraded by the greed of commercialism," and "tact and cleverness, brilliancy and beauty, exercise greater influence . . . than they do in most cities." [87]

Clearly those who extolled Washington, like those who denounced it, tended to see only limited sets of characteristics, and as a result of this astigmatism their descriptions were badly out of focus. Better perception would have revealed a city which was neither all gaudy and flamboyant, nor completely cultivated and genteel. The social structure contained several qualitatively different levels. As Laura Hawkins noted in *The Gilded Age;* Washington society was made up of three distinct components. There was the old aristocratic group which apotheosized its own cultivation, ancestoral roots, and distinguished record of public service. Families in this rigidly exclusive category were referred to as "Antiques." At the opposite pole was the "Aristocracy of the Parvenus" into which anyone might enter—provided, of course, he had money or official position. Origins counted for nothing and immediate assets were all. The "Antiques" somehow managed to ignore the "Parvenus," while the presumptious "Parvenus" laughed at the "Antiques," while secretly envying them. In between towered a middle group, "the best aristocracy of the three Washington castes, and the most powerful, by far . . . ." The heads of these families held posts in the legislative and executive branches of government. Educated, competent, and discreet, they "moved serenely in their wide orbit, confident in their own strength and well aware of the potency of their influence." [88]   The "Parvenus," as a result of their behavior, were most conspicuous, and as they asserted themselves the older residents became more withdrawn. "They were powerless to resist the tide of excess which so changed the character of their old home, and so protested against the orgies of the new comers by taking no part in them." [89]

Established social leaders retired from the social scene in order to raise the distinction between authentic quality and the artificial society of the newly rich. Setting themselves apart was a means for achieving exclusiveness. Collectively they comprised a polite social class, the best Washington had to offer. Withdrawal, moreover, seemed a sure way of overcoming the frustrations of cultural disharmony. Those dismayed by the texture of social life could form for themselves a cultivated circle which would serve as a real community of interest. This elite would be the embodiment of sophistication and simple dignity; a fairly close knit group, fastidious and highly civilized. Not only would its few members be treated to the charm of their own company, but together they could sneer at mediocrity.

For the most part these "cave-dwellers," as they came to be called, were located in the stately brick homes surrounding Lafayette Square. Ironically, this rectangular green opposite the White House had once been a graveyard. By the 1870's it provided the setting for a "series of mansions probably more historic than any other single group in the entire country," and it served as the last stronghold of a permanent residential society whose existence was independent of political change.[90] Here Twain's "Antiques" spent their evenings, entertaining each other while eschewing showy official receptions; and here developed a society praised as "the most delightful in the world."[91] Especially notable was the salon of Mr. and Mrs. Henry Adams, "an intellectual and high-bred center, a rendezvous for the best ton and the most acceptable people."[92] Although they sought isolation, members of this genteel group offset some of the flimsiness and fraud of capital life. Many were important figures in literature, science and art, and Washington as a whole shared the prestige of their intellectual amusements.

Coincident with this drive for social order, and the creation of a cultivated elite, was Washington's emergence as a hub of scientific enterprise. Here was a subtle analogy to the more obvious post-war industrialization that was going on elsewhere. The increasing scope of government science and the booming productivity of American industry were both sure signs of progress. In 1886 Edward A. Atkinson, Boston textile manufacturer and statistician, reported that the past twenty years of industrial expansion justified a renewed faith in the nation's destiny.[93] At the same time it was estimated "that there are more men of distinction in science in Washington than any other city in the country."[94] Both statements reflect a pervasive assumption about significance of numbers. This was revealed in 1883 when Matthew Arnold visited Washington to lecture on "Literature and Science." Although no local intellectual was deemed worthy of sharing the platform with Arnold, considerable pride was derived from the fact that the audience contained two dozen scientists from the Smithsonian Institution alone.[95]

One contemporary announced the arrival of a "new era," declaring that "there seems reason to anticipate that in time our capital city of Washington will come to be as well known as a centre of literature and art, as it is now recognized as the centre of statesmanship, law and science."[96] Another observer boasted that as soon as its social, political, and intellectual forces were fused into an ordered whole, Washington would stand as "the most superb manifestation of civilization."[97]

Such lofty expectations reflected the ambitious plans of the scientists, educators, and men of specialized scholarship who had gravitated to Washington during the Civil War decade and afterward sought to make the seat of government into the capital of national culture. When Anna E. Dickinson declared her "unlimited belief in its [Washington's] capacity to do anything," she actually was giving voice to the conviction held by local savants that the city's natural capacity for advancing culture was infinite, and that once its resources were tapped Washington would become "the intellectual mecca of the civilized world."[98]   Certain interconnected factors appeared to justify this optimistic view.

With the expansion of government agencies and quasi-governmental institutions, promising young men were attracted to Washington in greater numbers than ever before. Many worked for newly created bodies such as the United States Geological Survey, Army Medical Museum, United States Fish Commission, Department of Agriculture, and the Smithsonian's Bureau of Ethnology, The Smithsonian itself broadened the scope of its activities during this period, as did other pre-war institutions such as the Coast Survey, the Signal Service, the Light House Board, the Patent Office, and the Naval Observatory. Thus Washington took on stature as a locus of scientific training and research, and, rather quickly, acquired the reputation of being a "unique and collossal 'education plant.' "[99] Gilded Age Washington looked like the ideal time and place for what Daniel Coit Gilman called "young men bent on progress," and scores of them hastened to take advantage of the situation both for themselves and for the nation.[100] Indeed, with its potentially fine national libraries, art collections, museums, educational facilities, and a permanent corps of scientific and literary men there seemed no reason to doubt that Washington could take the lead in promoting all departments of knowledge and enhancing American culture. This vision was sustained by postwar nationalism, according to which the Capital was conceived of as the heart of future advancement. Consequently, Washington and its institutions became vastly important, as illustrated by Francis Lieber's statement to the Librarian of Congress when donating some books.

I have taken a pleasure in inscribing in these volumes "To the National Library." It is not the official name, but I take the liberty. It is the name you have to come to. Library of Congress was good enough in Jeffersonian times; but is not now after the war . . . I give these books on account of the Nationality in your library, and not of its Congressionality.[101]

Washington after the Civil War presented a portrait full of light and shadows. It was at once a "great and wicked" city mirroring the best and worst of the period.[102] In certain respects its culture was singularly inelegant. Epitomized by rough men of new wealth it seemed materialistic, tasteless, and thoroughly devoid of purpose. Custodians of genteel culture and social critics were scornful of this "aristocracy of shoddy." They had looked forward with hope and optimism to the post-bellum era which, they confidently felt, was destined to be of high moral purpose and spiritual greatness. But the war years had had a greater effect in whetting selfish appetites than in heightening idealistic fervor. During the general pursuit of earthly riches traditional values were rudely trampled.

At first glance Washington looked no more inspiring than the rest of the nation. Its society was of a low caliber and its luminaries were often coarse and vapid. Some sensitive Washingtonians sought to ameliorate this condition by resurrecting forgotten rules of etiquette. Others, who were pessimistic about possibilities for overall improvement, retreated into a social circle of their own choosing. But Washington also contained a powerful "middle aristocracy," as Twain labeled it, in which could be found many of the foremost intellectuals of the late nineteenth century. These men were deeply, if quietly, involved in public life, and together they added an important dimension to late nineteenth century culture. Their first great achievement was the ordering of Washington's intellectual community.

NOTES TO CHAPTER 1

1. Louis B. Wright, "Ivory Towers—A National Imperative," *The Tenth Cosmos Club Award* (Washington, D. C., 1973), p. 8; Henry Allen Moe, "On the Need for an Aristocracy," *The Second Cosmos Club Award* (Washington, D. C., 1965), pp. 7, 18.

2. Henry Adams to Charles Francis Adams, Jr., November 21, 1862, *A Cycle of Adams Letters, 1861-1865,* ed. Worthington Chauncy Ford (Boston, 1920), I, 196.

3. [Mark Twain], "The Curious Republic of Gondour," *Atlantic Monthly,* XXXVI (October, 1873), 461-462.

4. Simon Newcomb, "Exact Science in America," *North American Review,* CXIX (October, 1874), 286-308, and "Abstract Science in America, 1776-1876," *ibid.,* CXXII (January, 1876), 88-123, an insightful critique of Newcomb's strictures against national science may be found in Edward Lurie, "An Interpretation of Science in the Nineteenth Century: A Study in History and Historiography," *Journal of World History,* VIII (1965), 685-688.

5. Charles Francis Adams, Jr. to Carl Schurz, March 17, 1873, Schurz Papers, XIX, Manuscript Division, Library of Congress (henceforth LC); for an estimate of its importance in modern times see Waldo G. Leland, "The Cosmos Club and the Nation," November 16, 1943 (in the History File of the Cosmos Club).

6. Edwin P. Whipple, *Sucess and Its Conditions* (Boston, 1899), pp. 289-294.

7. William Dean Howells, *The Rise of Silas Lapham* (Boston, 1885; Rinehart edn., New York, 1949), p. 66.

8. Quoted in Edward Chase Kirland, *Charles Francis Adams, Jr., 1835-1915: The Patrician at Bay* (Cambridge, Mass., 1965), pp. 79-80.

9. Charles Eliot Norton to Thomas Carlyle, November 16, 1873, *Letters of Charles Eliot Norton,* eds. Sara Norton and M. A. DeWolfe Howe (Boston, 1913), II, 18; Geoffrey T. Blodgett, "The Mind of the Boston Mugwump," *Mississippi Valley Historical Review,* XLVIII (March, 1962), 616.

10. [Clarence King], "Style and the Monument," *North American Review,* CXLI (November, 1885), 443.

11. Charles Eliot Norton, "The Intellectual Life of America," *New Princeton Review,* n.s., VI (November, 1888), 315, 321-322.

12. Quoted in Kermit Vanderbilt, *Charles Eliot Norton: Apostle of Culture in a Democracy* (Cambridge, Mass., 1959), p. 70.

13. Diary of Mary Henry, January 4, 1865, II, Smithsonian Institution Archives; George M. Fredrickson, *The Inner Civil War: Northern Intellectuals and the Crisis of the Union* (New York, 1965), p. 74.

14. William M. Armstrong, "The Freedmen's Movement and the Founding of the *Nation,*" *Journal of American History,* LIII (March 1967), 710-715; John William DeForest, *Miss Ravenel's Conversion from Secession to Loyalty* (New York, 1867; Rinehart edn., New York, 1964), p. 461; John Michael Tomsich, "The Genteel Tradition in America, 1850-1910" (unpublished Ph.D. dissertation, Department of History, University of Wisconsin, 1963), p. 175; John G. Sproat, *"The Best Men": Liberal Reformers in the Gilded Age* (New York, 1968), p. 6; Geoffrey Blodgett, "Reform Thought and the Genteel Tradition," *The Gilded Age,* rev. and enl. edn., ed. H. Wayne Morgan (Syracuse, N. Y., 1970), p. 61; Robert L. Beisner, *Twelve Against Empire: The Anti-Imperialists, 1898-1900* (New York, 1968), pp. 53-83.

15. Martin B. Duberman, *James Russell Lowell* (Boston, 1966), pp. 232-233; Vanderbilt, *Norton,* pp. 106-112.

16. Norton to Carlyle, November 16, 1873, *Letters of Norton,* II, 18; John Tomsich, *A Genteel Endeavor: American Culture and Politics in the Gilded Age* (Stanford, Calif., 1971), pp. 58-64.

17. Mark Van Doren (ed.), *The Portable Walt Whitman* (New York, 1945), p. 400.

18. Sproat, *"The Best Men";* Blodgett, "Reform Thought and the Genteel Tradition," p. 60; John Tomsich, *A Genteel Endeavor.*

19. Quoted in Charles A. Beard and Mary K. Beard, *The American Spirit: A Study of the Idea of Civilization in the United States* (New York, 1942), pp. 373-374.

20. Quoted in Harry Barnard, *Rutherford B. Hayes and His America* (Indianapolis, Ind., 1954), p. 215.

21. Henry James, *The American* (Boston, 1877; Laurel edn., New York, 1960), pp. 249-250; Kermit Vanderbilt, "James, Fitzgerald, and the American Self-Image," *The Massachusetts Review,* VI (Winter-Spring, 1965), 289-304.

22. Quoted in David Lindsey, *"Sunset" Cox: Irrepressible Democrat* (Detroit, 1959), p. 135.

23. Quoted in Dixon Wector, *The Saga of American Society: A Record of Social Aspiration, 1607-1937* (New York, 1937), p. 176.

24. Michael Walzer, "Puritanism as a Revolutionary Ideology," *History and Theory,* III (1963), 77.

25. Perry Miller, *The New England Mind: From Colony to Province* (Cambridge, Mass., 1953; Beacon Paperback edn., Boston, 1961), pp. 3-4, 307-308.

26. Fred Somkin, *Unquiet Eagle: Memory and Desire in the Idea of American Freedom, 1815-1860* (Ithaca, N. Y., 1967), pp. 16-17.

27. Quoted in William E. Bridges, "Warm Hearth, Cold World: Social Perspectives on the Household Poets," *American Quarterly,* XXI (Winter, 1969), 773.

28. Joseph G. Baldwin, *The Flush Times of Alabama and Mississippi: A Series of Sketches* (New York, 1853; Hill & Wang edn., New York, 1957), p. 38.

29. Quoted in Russell Lynes, *The Tastemakers* (New York, 1949), p. 8.

30. Quoted in Allan Nevins, *Abram S. Hewitt, with Some Account of Peter Cooper* (New York, 1935), p. 95.

31. William R. Taylor, *Cavalier and Yankee: The Old South and American National Character* (London, 1963), pp. 96-101, see also, pp. 18, 126-128, 334; Somkin, *Unquiet Eagle,* pp. 11-34.

32. "Lecture on the Times," December 2, 1841, *The Prose Works of Ralph Waldo Emerson* (Boston, 1870), I, 154.

33. Bernard DeVoto (ed.), *Mark Twain in Eruption: Hitherto Unpublished*

Pages About Men and Events (New York, 1940; Capricorn Books edn., 1968), p. 77; Rev. David Macrae, *The Americans at Home: Pen-and-Ink Sketches of American Men, Manners, and Institutions* (Glasgow, 1875), pp. 26-27.

34. Frederic Cople Jaher, *Doubters and Dissenters: Cataclysmic Thought in America, 1885-1918* (New York, 1964); Herbert G. Gutman, "Protestantism and the American Labor Movement: The Christian Spirit in the Gilded Age," *American Historical Review*, LXXII (October, 1966), 81-82.

35. Francis A. Walker, "Our Population in 1900," *Atlantic Monthly*, XXXII (October, 1873), 492-493.

36. George M. Beard, "Causes of American Nervousness," in Henry Nash Smith (ed.), *Popular Culture and Industrialism, 1865-1890* (Garden City, N. Y., 1967), pp. 57-70; Donald Meyer, *The Positive Thinkers: A Study of the American Quest for Health, Wealth, and Personal Power from Mary Baker Eddy to Norman Vincent Peale* (Garden City, N. Y., 1965), pp. 21-31; Philip P. Wiener, "G. M. Beard and Freud on 'American Nervousness,' " *Journal of the History of Ideas*, XVII (April, 1956), 269-274; Charles E. Rosenberg, "The Place of George M. Beard in Nineteenth Century Psychiatry," *Bulletin of the History of Medicine*, XXXVI (May-June, 1962), 245-259.

37. Walker, *Atlantic Monthly*, XXXII, 494.

38. "Mr. Walter Camp, for so many years associated with Yale athletics, confirms the opinion of others that Walker looked on football or baseball as a matter of vital importance because of its effect upon the morale of the youth concerned. He had no patience with the diletante attitude which regards a game as a means of passing the time, or with the utilitarian point of view which looks upon it simply as a pleasant method of securing exercise." James Phinney Munroe, *A Life of Francis Amasa Walker* (New York, 1923), pp. 151-152; Fredrickson, *Inner Civil War* pp. 223-224.

39. Walker, *Atlantic Monthly*, XXXII, 495.

40. Henry Adams, *The Education of Henry Adams: An Autobiography* (Boston, 1918; Sentry edn., Cambridge, Mass., 1961), p. 237.

41. Blodgett, "Reform Thought and the Genteel Tradition," pp. 56, 73; Walker Rumble, "Rectitude and Reform: Charles T. Bonaparte and the Politics of Gentility, 1851-1921" (unpublished Ph.D. dissertation, Department of History, University of Maryland, 1970), pp. 73-75; the cultural crisis of the post-

Civil War era, and the breakdown of the Brahmin code of values, "produced the First lost generation of Americans," Barbara Miller Solomon, *Ancestors and Immigrants: A Changing New England Tradition* (Cambridge, Mass., 1956; Phoenix edn., 1972), p. 42.

42. Thomas Wentworth Higginson to his sister [Anna Higginson?], August 6, 1883, *Letters and Journals of Thomas Wentworth Higginson, 1846-1906,* ed. Mary Thacher Higginson (Boston, 1921), 322-323.

43. Quoted in Blodgett, "Reform Thought and the Genteel Tradition," p. 67.

44. Martin B. Duberman, *Charles Francis Adams, 1807-1886* (Cambridge, Mass., 1960), p. 337; his son, Charles Francis, Jr., was equally "impatient with 'chance,' 'anarchy,' 'chaos,' words constantly at the end of his pen;" Edward C. Kirkland, *Business in the Gilded Age: The Conservatives' Balance Sheet* (Madison, Wisc., 1952), p. 10.

45. Although Norton and Walker did not duplicate Adams's attempts to construct a systematic theory of decay, they obviously adhered to an anti-Comtian linear view of history and would have agreed with Adams that the deceleration of human progress resulted from a decrease of the energy that was vital to its continuance. Adams's historical speculations are critically assessed in William H. Jordy, *Henry Adams: Scientific Historian* (New Haven, Conn., 1952), pp. 121-255.

46. John W. Forney, *Anecdotes of Public Men* (New York, 1873), p. 352.

47. Quoted in James H. Whyte, *The Uncivil War: Washington During the Reconstruction, 1865-1878* (New York, 1958), p. 17.

48. Helen Nicolay, *Sixty Years of the Literary Society* (Washington, D. C., 1934), p. 4; Whyte, *Uncivil War,* pp. 13-17, 178-183.

49. Frances Carpenter (ed.), *Carp's Washington* (New York, 1960), pp. 87, 90; "Frank G. Carpenter," *Cosmos Club Bulletin,* II (July, 1949), 84.

50. Ben Perley Poore, *Perley's Reminiscences of Sixty Years in the National Metropolis* (Philadelphia, 1886), II, p. 527.

51. Jane W. Gemmill, *Notes on Washington, or Six Years at the National Capital* (Philadelphia, 1884), p. 80; see also George Alfred Townsend, *Washington, Outside and Inside* (Hartford, Conn., 1873), p. 684.

52. *Carp's Washington,* p. 110.

53. *Ibid.,* p. 89.

54. Adams, *Education,* p. 243.

55. John B. Ellis, *The Sights and Secrets of the National Capital: A Work Descriptive of Washington City in All Its Various Phases* (Chicago, 1869), p. 55.

56. Albert W. Atwood, *Gallaudet College, Its First One Hundred Years* (Lancaster, Pa., 1964), p. 16.

57. Julia Ward Howe, *Reminiscences, 1819-1899* (Boston, 1899), p. 269.

58. Gail Hamilton, "The Display of Washington Society: Considered as the Origin of Evil in the Universe," *Galaxy,* XXI (June, 1878), 762.

59. Harriett Blaine to Walker Blaine, March 18, 1872, *Letters of Mrs. James G. Blaine,* ed. Harriett S. Blaine Beale (New York, 1908), I, 105; Mrs. John A. Logan, *Reminiscences of a Soldier's Wife: An Autobiography* (New York, 1913), p. 239; Arinori Mori, *Life and Resources in America* (Washington, D. C., 1871), pp. 19-20; Allan Nevins, *Hamilton Fish: The Inner History of the Grant Administration* (New York, 1936; rev. ed., 1957), II, 568-570; a more credible estimate of senators' standards of living is contained in David J. Rothman, *Politics and Power: The United States Senate, 1869-1901* (Cambridge, Mass., 1966), pp. 137-143.

60. James A. Rawley, *Edwin D. Morgan, 1811-1883: Merchant in Politics* (New York, 1955), pp. 203-204.

61. Hamilton, *Galaxy,* XXI, 762.

62. Townsend, *Washington,* p. 684.

63. Henry Adams, *Democracy, an American Novel* (New York, 1880; Signet Classic edn., New York, 1961), pp. 20-21.

64. Emily Edson Briggs, *The Olivia Letters: Being Some History of Washington City for Forty Years as Told by the Letters of a Newspaper Correspondent* (New York, 1906), pp. 199-207; "Life at the National Capital," *Lippincott's Magazine of Popular Literature and Science,* XII (December, 1873), 658-659.

65. Mary Clemmer Ames, *Ten Years in Washington: Life and Scenes in the National Capital, as a Woman Sees Them* (Hartford, Conn., 1874), p. 245; Maurice Francis Egan, *Recollections of a Happy Life* (New York, 1924), pp. 62-63; Marian Adams to Dear Pater, January 18, 1882, *The Letters of Mrs. Henry Adams,* ed. Ward Thoron (Boston, 1936), p. 328.

66. Logan, *Reminiscences,* p. 346.

67. Rufus Rockwell Wilson, *Washington the Capital City, and Its Part in the History of the Nation* (Philadelphia, 1901), II, 343.

68. William B. Hesseltine, *Ulysses S. Grant: Politican* (New York, 1935), pp. 299-300.

69. Sarah G. Bowerman, "Sarah Madeleine Vinton Dahlgren," *Dictionary of American Biography,* eds. Allen Johnson and Dumas Malone (New York, 1959), III, 31-32; Madeleine V. Dahlgren to Horatio King, February 11, 1874, and May 5, 1874, King Papers, VI, LC; Charles Vandersee, "The Pursuit of Culture in Adams' *Democracy," American Quarterly,* XIX (Summer, 1967), 239-248.

70. Mrs. W. Chapin Huntington, "Ladies of the Literary," read before the Literary Society of Washington, January 9, 1965, Literary Society Papers, LC; Diary of Lucretia R. Garfield, March 19, 1881, Garfield Papers, LC.

71. Daily Record and Household Expenses and Personal Social Register, 1878-1881: Madeleine Vinton Dahlgren Papers, New York Public Library; Margaret Brent Downing, "Literary Landmarks," *Records of the Columbia Historical Society,* XIX (Washington, D. C., 1916), 50.

72. Mary Reed Bobbitt (comp.), *A Bibliography of Etiquette Books in America Before 1900* (New York, 1947), p. 3.

73. Arthur M. Schlesinger, *Learning How to Behave: A Historical Study of American Etiquette Books* (New York, 1946), pp. 32-37.

74. Madeleine Vinton Dahlgren, *Etiquette of Social Life in Washington,* 4th edn. (Washington, D. C., 1876), p. 13.

75. *Lippincott's Magazine,* XII, 657.

76. Dahlgren, *Etiquette,* p. 15. The first president actually was invoked as part of the campaign to improve taste and conduct. Appearing within a span of four

years were: *George Washington's Fifty-Seven Rules of Behavior* (1886); *Washington's Rules of Civility and Decent Behavior in Company and Conversation* (1888); *George Washington's Rules of Civility Traced to Their Sources* (1890).

77. George Santayana, *Persons and Places: The Background of My Life* (New York, 1944), pp. 203-204.

78. Wilcomb E. Washburn, "Manuscripts and Manufacts," *American Archivist,* XXVII (April, 1964), 248.

79. For a discussion of the concept of disintegration and reintegration see Rowland Berthoff, "The American Social Order: A Conservative Hypothesis," *American Historical Review,* LXV (April, 1960), 495-514.

80. Marian Gouverneur, *As I Remember: Recollections of American Society During the Nineteenth Century* (New York, 1911), p. 360.

81. Egan, *Recollections,* p. 64.

82. Wilson, *Washington,* II, 393.

83. Quoted in Leon Edel, *Henry James: The Middle Years, 1884-1894* (Philadelphia, 1962), p. 30.

84. Remarks by Henry S. Pritchett, *The Fiftieth Anniversary of the Founding of the Cosmos Club, 1878-1928* (Washington, D. C., 1929), p. 5, also quoted in Abraham Flexner, *Henry S. Pritchett, A Biography* (New York, 1943), p. 63.

85. Mrs. William Howard Taft, *Recollections of Full Years* (New York, 1914), p. 27.

86. Festus P. Summers (ed.), *The Cabinet Diary of William L. Wilson, 1896-1897* (Chapel Hill, N. C., 1957), January 15, 1896, pp. 9-10.

87. A. Maurice Low, "Washington: The City of Leisure," *Atlantic Monthly,* LXXXVI (December, 1900), 768-775.

88. Mark Twain and Charles Dudley Warner, *The Gilded Age: A Tale of To-Day* (Hartford, Conn.,1873, 1902), pp. 295-296, 311-312.

89. Edward Winslow Martin, *Behind the Scenes in Washington* (Washington, D.

C., 1873), p. 48; Constance McLaughlin Green, *Washington: Village and Capital, 1800-1878* (Princeton, N. J.), I, 375-376.

90. Hal M. Smith, "Historic Washington Homes," *Records of the Columbia Historical Society,* XI (Washington, D. C., 1908), 244; Gist Blair, "Lafayette Square," *ibid.,* XXVIII (Washington, D. C., 1926), 133-173; Marietta Minnigerode Andrews, *My Studio Window: Sketches of the Pageant of Washington Life* (New York, 1928), pp. 31-34.

91. "Washington Gossip," *Cincinnati Commercial,* November 9, 1876, xeroxed copy in the Rutherford B. Hayes Library.

92. Henry Watterson, *"Marse Henry," An Autobiography* (New York, 1919), II, 34-35.

93. Smith (ed.), *Popular Culture and Industrialism,* pp. xiv-xvi.

94. Poore, *Perley's Reminiscences,* II, 529.

95. James Dow McCallum, "The Apostle of Culture Meets America," *New England Quarterly,* II (July, 1929), 374-375.

96. I. Edwards Clarke, "The Conditions of Literature in Washington at the Time of the Founding of This Society," read before the Literary Society of Washington, January 21, 1899, Literary Society of Washington Papers, LC.

97. Ames, *Ten Years,* p. 255.

98. Anna E. Dickinson, *A Ragged Register (of People, Places and Opinions)* (New York, 1879), p. 183; Tallmadge A. Lambert, "Observations on the Development of the National Capital," *Records of the Columbia Historical Society,* II (Washington, D. C., 1899), 291.

99. James C. Welling to Daniel C. Gilman, March 29, 1889, Gilman Papers, The Johns Hopkins University Library.

100. On Gilman's optimism after the war see Hugh Hawkins, *Pioneer: A History of The Johns Hopkins University, 1874-1889* (Ithaca, N. Y., 1960), p. 18.

101. Francis Lieber to Ainsworth R. Spofford, May 20, 1870, Spofford Papers, LC; Fredrickson, *Inner Civil War,* p. 184.

102. Harriett Blaine to Walker Blaine, May 27, 1869, *Letters of Mrs. Blaine,* I, 10.

2

Elegant Circles

Sensitive observers of post-war Washington usually were impressed by the city's ability to foster scientific and literary societies. These organizations imposed a modicum of order on an otherwise formless urban culture. They also epitomized a flourishing interest in aspects of the mind and spirit. Then, as now, intellectual pretentions did not guarantee excellence. In the rash of associations that were hastily established during this period there could always be found poor imitations of the authentic.

This unhappy condition was due to the fact that membership in a scientific or literary society had symbolic as well as intrinsic value, and probably more people were allured by the former than the latter motive. Those in the genteel class, attempting to set themselves apart from the Gilded Age barbarians, found such groups decidedly useful. Literature as an avocation had traditionally served to designate a gentleman; it was the universally acknowledged badge of breeding and leisure. Science in post-war America brought even higher social dividends. To be deeply interested in science was to be "cultivated." Devotion to its abstractions showed that one eschewed material concerns. The educated thus sought to emphasize their distinctiveness by forming and joining literary and scientific societies.[1]

The newly rich too considered identification with intellectually oriented groups just as important. Such affiliations offset the lack of family background in the pursuit of social position. Much of the popularity of scientific and literary societies stemmed from the status they automatically bestowed.

Farsighted and practical individuals who organized learned societies after the Civil War knew that the quest for connections could redound to

31

their advantage. As a result, men of means often became the principal benefactors of scientific and literary associations. When Franz Boas solicited advice about starting an ethnological society in New York, he was reminded that "You want patrons as well as talkers, men who like to see their names among intellectual people."[2] But not all the status seekers were drawn into intellectually respectable groups. Many developed circles of their own, and as the years passed, and these multiplied, Washington was surfeited with lowbrow institutions.

One person who regarded this plethora of organizations as highly amusing was Lillie de Hegermann-Lindencrone, the American born wife of the Danish minister to the United States. She was a member of several different circles and even her black valet belonged to a Browning-Tennyson reading club. He used to wear the club decoration in his buttonhole while serving formal dinners. Often guests identified it as the French Legion of Honor, and once he was mistaken for the minister from Haiti.[3] Mme. de Hegermann-Lindencrone's letters from the Capital contain reports of "Sunday evenings" at Mary Isabella Robeson's, the wife of George Maxwell Robeson, a wealthy lawyer from New Jersey, Republican wheelhorse, and Grant's Secretary of the Navy. Together they cut an impressive figure, and their evenings were tailor-made for conducting after-hours political business. Though a member of the musical section of the Literary Society of Washington, the hostess did not allow music to be played on those evenings because she felt it limited conversation. The whole point was to provide a setting for quiet discussion of the sort which took place among Republican congressional leaders in March 1877 concerning the new Hayes administration and Reconstruction policy.[4] Outside of the Robeson's, Washington society seemed a farce. The only way to accommodate oneself to it, concluded Mme. de Hegermann-Lindencrone, was to be facetious. In 1879, she and a few intimates (Carl Schurz among them) lightheartedly organized the National Rational International Dining Club. There were bylaws and officers—"who had the job of recognizing and calling attention to the jokes."[5]

A serious bid to build a literary community was exemplified by the salon presided over by Horatio King. For King, a former cabinet officer and long time resident, the cultivation of intellect became his major purpose in life. Born and raised on a farm near Paris, Maine he received little formal instruction beyond what the common schools could provide. The breadth of his knowledge was almost entirely self-acquired. He did not attend Bowdoin College, which during the first third of the nineteenth century was regarded as the Athens of northern New England. Had he done so, he would have known the celebrated company of William Pitt Fessenden, Nathaniel Hawthorne, Henry Wadsworth Longfellow, Franklin Pierce, and Calvin Stowe. Instead, he went to work as a printer's devil, and like some of his friends who hailed from the inverted triangle extending between New Hampshire and the Kennebec River—notably Hannibal Hamlin, Anson Morrill, and Elihu Washburne and his brothers Cadwallader and Israel—King made his mark without benefit of higher education. Rather than hindering his progress, this void inspired him to map out a course of personal study that covered a broad range of subjects.

Before they had reached twenty years of age, he and future vice-president Hamlin became owners of their hometown newspaper, the *Jeffersonian,* but in 1830 King took over as its editor and sole proprietor. Under his management the paper assumed a pro-Jacksonian position, a loyalty which brought about his advancement to Washington. In 1839, Amos Kendall rewarded him with a clerk's position in the Post Office Department. King then began a steady climb leading to the postmaster generalship. Upon retirement, in 1861, he devoted himself to community service, most significantly as secretary of the Washington Monument Society. As secretary he was instrumental in bringing the Society's main project to completion. Horatio King's rise from farm boy to member of the government reaffirmed the national faith in equality of opportunity and individual success. Beyond that it placed him in the front rank of Washington society after the Civil War, and given his commitment to learning, it was natural that he would use this position in an endeavor to elevate cultural standards.[6]

Seeking to fulfill the responsibilities of social leadership, King, late in 1869, began holding what were known as "literary reunions." These assemblies were held at the pleasure of the host. Attendance was by invitation only, and on several occasions visitors who appeared without one of King's handsomely engraved cards found the portal barred. Mrs. Henry Rowe Schoolcraft, widow of the famed ethnologist, was turned away, and King showed no compunction about refusing a friend who requested admission. On this point King was unyielding—regardless of the mortification inflicted. When pressed for a justification of his policy, he would explain that his house was simply too small to accommodate more than the anticipated number.[7] However, there was also the ulterior motive of insuring that without exception guests would be persons of influence and standing. King's objective was to provide an atmosphere for "free and pleasant intercourse among the educated and accomplished."[8] Simply put, this meant excluding lightweights by making the reunions highly selective.

There had been literary groups at the Capital before, but, as Mrs. School-craft painfully discovered, King's was the first to consider the quality of its members a *sine qua non*.[9]

This is not to say that King welcomed only authors and critics. Had he done so his reunions would have failed for want of participants. Gilded Age Washington was notably lacking in prestigious literary figures. Most writers and scholars of distinction were either transient lecturers or tempo-rary residents. George William Curtis often spent an evening at King's when he visited Washington, and Moses Coit Tyler, then commencing what would prove to be his landmark study of colonial American litera-ture, addressed the King group in January, 1871. Lew Wallace frequented reunions during 1873 while working at the Library of Congress prepara-tory to writing *Ben-Hur,* but his stay was brief and when it ended King's circle lost one of its few famous authors. In fact, the composition of the reunions was less artistic than governmental, which was to be expected considering what King sought to accomplish. He hoped that his gatherings might gain public attention, set an example others would follow, and thereby create a countervailing force against what he pointedly referred to as "the crowded and expensive 'receptions' held at unreasonable hours and which are so unnecessary and unreasonable in almost every respect."[10] It was imperative to have celebrities no matter how tenuous their with *belles lettres*.

Within the context of Washington this meant primarily office holders or persons like King who had occupied positions in the government. Literary qualifications counted for less than political stature. Over the years most well known politicians were prevailed upon to attend. President Grant, for example, was promised "a more *cordial,* if not as *warm* and *brilliant* a re-ception as he received at Fort Donaldson, Vicksburg and Richmond,"[11] while an overture to President Hayes contained the assurance that "literary exercises would not last more than an hour."[12]

Stressing the felicity of his reunions was one way King tried to attract important personalities; another was by making certain that his gatherings stayed apolitical. With the conviction that art and politics do not mix, he was scrupulously careful to remain free from partisanship.[13] Accordingly King was able to bring under one roof Alexander Stephens and Grand Army of the Republic stalwart Lucius Fairchild, along with such antago-nists as Thomas A. Hendricks and Hannibal Hamlin; Samuel Randall and Schuyler Colfax. Although an ardent Democrat, King abided by the same standard he set for others. As if to underscore this he composed an affec-

tionate tribute to Justin Morrill, grand old man of the Republican party,
on the latter's seventy-fifth birthday:

> One year ago, came not a few
>   Within your open door,
> Exulting at the thought that you
>   Were young at sev'nty-four.
> Again we greet you with delight,
>   While we ourselves survive,
> That you are well and bright to-night,
>   And young at sev'nty-five.
> Meantime, your old Green Mountain State,
>   By resolution firm,
> Hath wisely voted you, of late,
>   Another six years' term.
> Hence, you are bound as all must see,
>   To fill the term begun,
> And ne'er forget, at least to be
>   Still young at eighty-one.[14]

James Buchanan had every right to tell King "you were more distinguished as assistant postmaster general and as chief of the department than you will ever become as a poet."[15] With King's verse as a case in point, it is easy to see why the atmosphere of his reunions more closely resembled exracurricular meetings of public officials than seminars of literati. The short lectures were sometimes witty, but never erudite, complicated, or discussed afterward. The brevity of programs was what speakers emphasized most when proposing topics for King's approval: "I would like much to offer my lecture on 'Theory and Practice,' or 'The Practical Man' .... It is short—by far the shortest lecture I have," wrote one candidate; another volunteered to read a new poem, "A True History of Jack and Gill [sic]," which could be cut from twenty to ten minutes should that suit King's pleasure.[16] In addition to chosing their subjects speakers also named their audiences by submitting guest lists which King would ratify. All this made for evenings that were congenial and relaxing if not intellectually incandescent.

Yet everything indicates that this mode was exactly what King desired. "Social intercourse," he proclaimed, was "the *main object* of these receptions," and considering what he set out to accomplish, the literary reunions were eminently successful.[17] By the mid-seventies they occupied a fixed position in the social and intellectual life of the Capital City. Reflecting what King termed "the cultivated sense of the community," they were characterized by stateliness, which distinguished them from the distasteful fare of Gilded Age culture.[18] Every opportunity was seized to shun ostentation, as King pointed out in a note to a new guest: "We expect our friends to come in their ordinary calling costume—not at all as to a 'dress party.' We ask them to step up to the third story and lay off their hats, bonnet, and over dress, and we receive them without any display in the parlor."[19] By using the gaudy receptions as a foil, King's literary reunions became models of dignity and mediums for improving the tone of local society. Nothing could have pleased him more than when he was informed that his meetings had come to constitute one of the Capital's most "elegant circles."[20]

Elegant the reunions may have been, and certainly they had a desirable effect on taste and conduct, but as a force in the development of America's literary tradition the King group was insignificant. To declare that King succeeded in "concentrating and developping [sic] Literary talent, at the National Metropolis," claimed too much for his reunions, and there simply is no hard evidence to support the assertion that through his efforts Washington became a fount of national influence.[21] This aggregation was plainly not on a par with Boston's Saturday Club, whose membership roster of Emerson, Hawthorne, Howells, Holmes, Longfellow, Motley, Prescott, Lowell, Whittier, and others approximated a "Who's Who" of American letters. With the possible exception of the reunions' strict simplicity and concise programs, which in a way mirrored the new terseness in fiction, King's group failed to ripple the stream of literary history.[22]

In the eyes of contemporary Washingtonians the reunions appeared to be a major achievement. If some were prone to exaggerate their significance, it was because the gatherings brought a refreshing change in the local atmosphere and held much promise for the future. At last it seemed that the cherished hope for an intellectual community in the Capital might be fulfilled; that through learned institutions formed to stabilize Gilded Age culture there would be laid a foundation for the national establishment of science and literature which men had yearned for in earlier times. King's group represented a step towards the realization of that dream. True, there was no organizational structure, no regular membership, no meeting schedule, no publication, and not even an official name. Yet these informal reunions showed that Washington was ripe for serious-minded associations. Entertainments designed for the benefit of close friends and the progress of Washington culture suggested the efficacy of intellectual bodies.

It may be assumed that John Jay Knox, a founder of the Cosmos Club, was influenced to some degree by his wife's musicales which yielded fascinating implications for the organization of Washington culture. Carrie Knox's elegant circle was noted for drawing together congressmen, cabinet members, scientists, Supreme Court justices, and various public administrators. Surely this lesson weighed on the mind of her husband when he decided to help create an elitist institution.[23] That there were irreducible differences between King's circle and Mrs. Knox's piano recitals on the one hand, and the Cosmos Club on the other, was true enough. Although the former groups suffered from a deficiency of talent, successor societies—notably those devoted to science—were increasingly professional in character and function.

The late 1880's witnessed a curtailment and finally a ceasing of the literary reunions. Part of the reason was that King found more and more of his time being monopolized by the Washington Monument Society. But that does not entirely explain why they were discontinued. Clearly the reunions had served their purpose, Washington was no longer the boorish backwater it had been in 1869. As a direct result of King's impetus there were now several other organizations which he had helped inspire and which in turn were endeavoring to build upon his success.

One such group was the Literary Society of Washington, which after the mid-seventies accelerated the drive for social order and intellectual advancement. "The Literary" (to use its properly abbreviated title)[24] grew up independently of King's circle and presented some marked contrasts to it. There were strong hints that the old postmaster general may have been one of its progenitors—especially since both took such pains to avow their commitment to art. Each sought to infuse Washington with the elegance that official society could never provide, and outwardly they went about gaining their mutual objective in the same way: by holding elite assemblies for the enjoyment and edification of themselves, while at the same time hoping that their examples would be widely emulated. The chief difference was internal, and because its organizational framework was better developed The Literary's influence was more enduring.[25] This resulted from the fact that as soon as The Literary was begun its early organizers faded into the background.

Numerous quasi-intellectual associations darted across the horizon of late nineteenth century culture; their progress was meteoric and when they vanished it was usually due to the lack of brilliance of their principal members. What helped sustain the Literary Society was the prestige of its leaders. Had it chosen to rely on those who did the original planning its life span probably would have been as evanescent as many similar groups, for Esmeralda Boyle, Sara Carr Upton, and even Olive Risley Seward were amiable but relatively anonymous.

Of the three, Miss Seward was the best known. Hanson Risley, her father, was a lifelong ally of William Henry Seward who had provided him with a minor post in the Treasury. It was the daughter, however, whom Seward found the more interesting member of the family—indeed he was infatuated with her. Despite the forty-odd years separating their ages she returned his affections, and gradually they became constant companions. During the late sixties there were carriage rides and picnics along Rock Creek, evenings spent in studying the classics, trips together to upstate New York, a tour of the Orient, and embarrassing gossip about the aged widower cavorting with the rather pretty daughter of his associate. Apparently, the only way to continue the relationship and safeguard their reputations was adoption. Accordingly, after discussions with Hanson Risley and Seward's children, she took the name of her devoted admirer.[26]

Even before meeting Seward, Olive had shown a mildly intellectual bent. As a girl in New York City before the war she experienced the exciting receptions of the sisters Alice and Phoebe Cary, whose house on Twentieth Street was the center of a literary circle. Each Sunday evening, in the Cary's library, gathered a remarkable coterie of men and women noted for their grace, wit, and artistic sensibilities rather than mere social position. Though various shades of political persuasion were represented, the atmosphere never grew tense and the conversation was always stimulating.[27] Olive Risley Seward's eager participation in starting a similar group in Washington stemmed from glowing remembrances of times past, and the character of the new organization bore the stamp of her youthful impressions. It was in Miss Seward's home that plans for The Literary were first discussed, late in 1873, after which she slipped out of sight so that more illustrious personages could become the objects of attention.[28]

At this critical juncture John George Nicolay came forward and by his presence The Literary took on an aura of distinction. Nicolay had achieved prominence while serving with John Hay as President Lincoln's private secretary. Following the assassination he took charge of the American Consulate in Paris, and remained overseas until 1869. Paris, which he adored, proved to be the scene of repeated vexations when Nicolay was charged with incompetence by political intriguers who coveted his post.

Nor was life in the United States much happier. Ill health plagued him after he returned, the articles he wrote were indifferently received, and he was distraught by what seemed an ominous degeneration of the national character. Patriotism and idealism were shrouded in corruption, with conditions at the Capital City being bleakest of all. He longed for some way to ameliorate the situation, but what was to be done? Bequeathing to America a detailed portrait of Abraham Lincoln, one that would enshrine the Lincoln tradition by showing him to have been infinitely great offered possibilities for rekindling moral fervor.[29] Yet a work of this magnitude would be a long term project, leaving unanswered the need for an immediate remedy. He was therefore alacritous in accepting the invitation of the Washington Literary Society, a group that bid fair to enhance local culture and which, ultimately, owed as much to Nicolay as he to it.

In 1874 Nicolay was marshal of the Supreme Court, but his influence derived from his unofficial position as a resident Washington intellectual. This represented a personal triumph. Nicolay began life inauspiciously. His emergence as a social and intellectual leader was redolent of Horatio King's climb from obscurity. Except for a few basic differences their careers could be interchanged. Whereas King was a native Yankee, Nicolay emigrated from Germany to the Midwest. During the political maelstrom of the antebellum years King stayed with the Democrats while Nicolay became a Republican. But most other essentials were the same: fending for themselves as apprentice printers and rising to the top as young editors; cultivating literary interests and pursuing self-education; and entering government bureaucracy at low levels and becoming presidential confidants. Finally, both wrote favorable accounts of the administrations in which they served. Interestingly, there was little affection between them, and there was never the remotest possibility of collaboration. Working separately, however, they were each instrumental in guiding Washington's intellectual progress. This was especially true in the case of Nicolay, whose Society was more ambitious and required a more elaborate organization.[30]

Putting aside his drafts of the mammoth *Abraham Lincoln: A Biography,* Nicolay set to work writing a constitution for the Literary Society. Samuel Tyler, professor of law at Columbia College lent assistance. By the beginning of the 1875-76 season, the document was complete. It provided for a Society of thirty members (soon increased to forty) who would meet on alternate Saturday evenings for purposes of "literary and artistic improvement and entertainment." Governing power was delegated to a five member executive committee, elected annually, which would appoint all other officers and committees, choose meeting sites, have charge of programs, and approve nominations for membership. When vacancies occurred new members could be installed only by securing two sponsors within The Literary and after receiving a unanimous vote of the Executive Committee. This screening process implied standards which candidates had to meet, criteria for winnowing excellence from mediocrity. Personal wealth was irrelevant since there was no initiation fee, no dues, and hence, no treasury. So highly valued was the absence of financial requirements that when it became necessary to raise money for some special occasion, the Executive Committee asked for voluntary contributions instead of levying general assessments.[31]

The important question was whether the candidate could add something of literary or artistic substance to the Society. According to the constitution: "All members pledge themselves to contribute at least once in each year, as they may be invited by the Executive Committee, an original essay, poem, or translation." Obligatory participation signaled the uniqueness of the Literary Society and provided a basis for its founders to proclaim the opening of a new, exhilirating chapter in Washington's history.[32]

In an attempt to create optimum conditions for participation, and to insure that there would be an appropriate balance between writers and artists, the membership was divided into classes. On November 13, 1875, less than two weeks after the adoption of the constitution, it was resolved to have twenty-five literary members, ten painters, and five musicians. These rubrics were not always honored. Over the years there evolved a disproportionate number of the literary element—persons who were nominally writers no matter how infrequently their efforts appeared in print.

That many members had means of support other than their pens was evidenced by The Literary's occupational composition, which ranged from businessman and clergyman to diplomat, senator, and even president of the United States. The president automatically attained membership as an honorary associate, a classification which also applied to the chief justice, speaker of the House of Representatives, attorney general, and secretary of the Smithsonian Institution. In addition there were honorary associates whose high standing in the community made them desirable members. William Wilson Corcoran, Mrs. Rutherford B. Hayes, and Alexander Stephens, invested The Literary with riches both tangible and symbolic. This aspect of admissions policy did not adulterate the membership, however, since the total of honorary associates was not allowed to exceed one-quarter of the active members. Moreover, those in the special category tended to be more than social luminaries. Banker Corcoran was also a patron of the arts, and Congressman Stephens, who led his class at the University of Georgia, was publishing treatises on constitutional problems. Thus The Literary was consistent in its demand that members be contributors rather than figureheads.[33]

The Literary Society went farther than King's reunions toward achieving the happy combination of social repute and intellectual merit. Not only was this a boon in terms of the organization's image, it also meant that The Literary drew from a bounteous reservoir of talent. Joseph Henry was tapped to speak on the philosophy of science; John Wesley Powell about costumes of North American Indians; Edward M. Gallaudet described how deaf-mutes were educated; General Albert J. Myer, the Army's chief signal officer and a founder of the Weather Bureau, lectured on meteorological observations; and geologist Clarence Edward Dutton was asked to share his knowledge of western mountain ranges. There were writers such as Frances Hodgson Burnett, soon to gain fame as the author of *Little Lord Fauntleroy* (1886), Thomas Nelson Page, poet Richard Hovey, and Mrs. E. D. E. N. Southworth, the "most popular authoress in the annals of American publishing,"[34] to lead literary exercises. Members like Nicolay, who had lived abroad, sounded a cosmopolitan note in the proceedings. Shortly before becoming secretary of state, John W. Foster gave his impressions of Mexico where he had spent seven years as minister. George Kennan best known for his *Tent Life in Siberia* (1870), forcefully recounted the adventures of his Russian travels—including, on at least one occasion, his own renditions of chanted prayers and boat songs. Another time, for a talk on political prisioners, he came clad in the gray uniform, chains, and fetters worn by convicts in eastern Siberia. Kennan's enthusiasm both typified the spirit with which experts in various fields supported The Literary and demonstrated emphatically that these were the individuals who formed its backbone.[35]

Among the most esteemed of the members was James Garfield. Garfield, while still a congressman, began attending meetings the year after they started. In 1876 he joined the organization. Unfortunately the burden of public duties made his attendance irregular. During the season of 1877-78 he ran afoul of a new article in the constittion which stipulated that three successive unexplained absences would be penalized by expulsion. But the Sage of Mentor redeemed himself when he dutifully appeared at the next meeting and commented upon a paper concerning the habits of the aeronat spider. Thereafter he spoke frequently, and became such a valuable member that he was twice elected president. In fact, Garfield held

The Literary's highest office during his abbreviated term in the White House. Lucretia Garfield remained an honorary associate for thirty-six years following her husband's assassination, and the president's former secretary, Joseph Stanley-Brown, was subsequently accepted as a member. Soon after Garfield died, and on the fiftieth anniversary of his birth, commemorative exercises were held at the residence of Dr. Gallaudet. Eulogies and tributes were read including a poem by Mrs. Burnett. There were fond recollections of Garfield's contributions to the Literary Society, and a display of photographs and portraits by fellow members. This was the first meeting of its kind, a lasting memorial to one of the brightest lights in The Literary's early history.[36]

As a rule gatherings of The Literary were not this grand. The season extended from December through May with meetings held wherever facilities were available. Usually this meant assembling in members' homes, though sometimes space was provided at a site such as the Smithsonian or the Willard Hotel. Invariably the executive committee would alot two and a half hours for an evening's activities, and almost without fail the meetings continued well beyond the time for adjournment. It was common for the secretary to close the Minutes with: "At a late hour the Society adjourned," or, "The hour of midnight brought the time for parting." A meeting at Garrick Mallery's once lasted so long that streetcar riders found themselves stranded because the lines had stopped running for the night.[37] Invited guests were permitted, except at the first meeting in December, the annual business session and election of officers. Indeed, the opportunity to make the "acquaintance of a distinguished *artist, savan [sic], actor or actress or musician* who may be for a few days in town" rated high among The Literary's attributes.[38] In January 1882, a meeting at Francis Hodgson Burnett's home was enlived by Oscar Wilde, whom Mrs. Robeson had in tow during his tour of the Capital.[39] Famous visitors were encouraged to participate, and comments from the likes of George W. Cable, Samuel Clemens, and Moncure Daniel Conway made memorable evenings. But in the main regular members were responsible for The Literary's programs.[40]

The schedule devised by the executive committee called for two papers at each meeting. These, plus the critiques that followed, constituted the exercises in which literary members made their required contributions. As might be expected there was an enormous variety of topics and forms of presentation, and a qualitative unevenness in the papers themselves. Some of the better essays, poems, short stories, and descriptive sketches were later printed by the Literary Society. For the most part these still hold the reader's attention. On the other hand one begins to squirm just thinking about enduring "The Stony Brook and What It Said," by Peter Baumgras, or Annie Story's recitation of "When You and I Were Young Lad." The only stipulation about lectures was that they not exceed twenty minutes in length, otherwise speakers enjoyed absolute freedom. The monthly discussions were more regimented.[41]

Every third meeting was given over to general discussion of some subject which the executive committee announced in advance. No one was exempt from participation; artistic and musical members as well as those in the literary category were expected to have in hand prepared expositions on the topic. Five minutes were allowed for each speaker, his name being called by the president from an alphabetical membership list.[42] While the general discussions were more 'structured than the regular literary exercises the former showed an equal variety of subject matter. "What Desirable Social Elements are Endangered by the Rapid Advance of Civilization?"; "Who Were the Chief Promoters of American Independence?"; "The Character and Public Life of Jefferson"; "What Shall We Do With Our Leisure?"; and "The Influence of Fiction in Reform" were but a few of the problems discussed. The only topics excluded were those touching upon politics and religion.[43]

"In our literary symposia," emphasized an old member, "controversy has no place."[44] Whatever else might be said about the desires of the founders, they hardly included providing a forum for vigorous debate. "Our aim and purpose is to *assimilate contraries*," proclaimed Madeleine Vinton Dahlgren, The Literary's leading matriarch. "This Society claims to be neutral ground rather than a battlefield—for while a free expression of opinions is intended our discussions are expected to elicit truth."[45] Her's was the dominant voice in policy matters throughout the first phase—so much so, in fact, that this period came to be known as "The Protectorate." The decisiveness she manifested in *Etiquette of Social Life in Washington*, and the moral certitude that punctuated her short stories,[46] carried over to her tutelage of The Literary. Henry James has left a fictionalized portrait of her in *Pandora* in which a Mrs. Steuben, the martinet of Capital society whose home was a famous literary meeting place, ". . . was the widow of a commodore," and "had about her a positive strong odour of Washington."[47] Although she never became president (no woman ever did), Mrs. Dahlgren held sway over the executive committee and was able to usurp the role of permanent hostess. One founder even referred to it as the "Dahlgren Literary Society."[48] Officially banning controversy reflected her will and because she deemed the quest for truth and spirited debate incompatible she sought to gird The Literary against disruptive polemics.

Yet Mrs. Dahlgren's wishes were not always obeyed, and it would be a mistake to interpret the founders' professions of consensus to mean that meetings were subdued. On the contrary, a survey of the Minutes reveals that programs were punctuated by intense intellectual probing, challenging of entrenched orthodoxies, and discourse that was respectful but sometimes vehement. Certainly greater attention was paid to sensitive questions than Mrs. Dahlgren's statement implies.

In the spring of 1881 members listened attentively while H. Pelham Curtis translated *The Struggle for the Plea Guility,* a realistic German poem which, Secretary Theodore Dwight noted, "produced a deep impression. It was another reminder of the momentous social questions which are pressing for a solution at home and abroad." Earlier the discussion topic had been industrial employment, showing that The Literary was not averse to taking up provocative subjects. Nor were individual members evasive in handling delicate issues. George Kennan made no secret of his opposition to Czar Alexander III and repressions in Russia. After one lecture Samuel Clemens commented on the cruelty and tyranny described by Kennan, "and the apparent impossibility of effecting a change for the better in any way but by revolution." Talk of revolution, industrial violence, and domestic discord did not square with the soothing meetings idealized by Mrs. Dahlgren.[49]

In addition there was more healthy disagreement than The Literary's spokesmen chose to admit. When Clarence Dutton argued that there should be no limitations placed on the accumulation of wealth, because large fortunes were rewards for social usefulness, Henry Ulke retorted that economic inequality was the origin of much suffering. This prompted others to join in the dispute.[50]

At another meeting a heated debate ensued over the question of what caused poverty. I. Edwards Clarke offered an explanation which anticipated later denunciations of wealthy malefactors while Dr. Gallaudet maintained it was due to shiftlessness and a lack of thrift. Several concurred, calling attention to the Irish as a case in point. Socialists and anarchists were roundly condemned except by Ulke who once again epitomized the spirit of intellectual dissent.[51]

Quarrels over the relative merits of authors were also lively. During a session devoted to Browning, Augustus Heaton charged that his "Jacobin style was a defiance of the classic elegance and form of the highest masters of poetry." Then, pressing his attack, he likened Browning's poems to "a

mob entering a city pillaging attics and cellars on the way." This dispar-
agement was too much for Ainsworth Spofford, who sprang to the defense
by proclaiming him the "greatest dramatic poet since Shakespeare."[52] It
would seem that on many evenings the musical portion of the program
came as a welcome respite after the good natured—if tumultous—exchanges
of ideas.

Why was there so little candor about an aspect of the organization
which in the afterglow of history appears as one of its most commendable
features? The answer lies in the high premium accorded the image of elegance. Following in the footsteps of Horatio King the founders strove for
dignity while at the same time maintaining their guard against anything
that threatened to detract from the stately impression they had already
made. Ideally, meetings of The Literary were to be such that when one
entered he could feel himself passing from the hurly-burly world of politics
and commerce into an atmosphere of graceful tranquility. Not surprisingly, then, since their objective was the opposite of Gilded Age ostentation, the founders played down whatever might be construed as bad taste
or coarse behavior. This concern for refinement could be seen in The
Literary's practice of disregarding formal titles and military rank, a custom rigidly observed. Here was a patent reaction to those who inundated
Washington during and after the Civil War spangled with symbols of
importance. Literary Society members regarded such display as attempts
to veil inferiority. Hence they stripped off all artificial distinctions to better expose their true excellence. In much the same spirit it was decreed that
suppers provided by meeting hosts were to be only light repasts. Although
not readily admitted by the organization this rule was broken from time to
time, a further transgression against the ideal of absolute simplicity.[53]

It is ironic that while modesty and reticence received heavy stress
members were outspoken when describing the role of their organization in
post-bellum American culture. "It should aim at nothing less than to be
the center of the artistic and literary life of the Capital;" this was its
"inspiring motive."[54] If Washington was the intellectual hub of the
nation, then certainly the Literary Society must stand at the intellectual
center of Washington. "We desire to become a thought nucleus,"
announced Mrs. Dahlgren boldly.

This Capital is filled with representative men elected to mold the destinies of
this great nation, as also with men chosen to represent other nations near us.
It becomes then a center for forensic eloquence and of statecraft and diplo-
macy--shall it not as well become a focus of intellectual force in every

domain, and thus exert a corresponding power over the national will in the various departments of human knowledge? But such influence, to be felt, must be aggregated. With this view our Society seeks a solidarity of interest for the scientist, the scholar, the writer, and the artist.[55]

This declaration of intent deserves critical attention. Its central assumption was that "intellectual force" is no less important in the affairs of men than "statecraft." In America, mind must be made "a corresponding power" of politics. Indeed there exists a natural connection between the two which should be understood and cultivated. Bountiful returns await the nation if only thought and government could be harmonized. But how might this be brought to pass? How make intellect the equal partner of institutionalized political authority? To the founders of The Literary the solution was to be found in the establishment of an association of intellectuals; by the creation of an institution of broad culture that could take its place in an America which, at every turn, was becoming more rationalized—or more "aggregated" as Mrs. Dahlgren would have described it. She, of course, was not alone in perceiving that before intellectuals could influence national life it was first necessary to adopt the national mode of organization, to utilize the tactic of institutional development in order to achieve power. Others recognized this imperative and, with growing force, they too sought "a solidarity of interest for the scientist, the scholar, the writer, and the artist."

The Washington Literary Society set itself a formidable task. The dimension of its success, however, is not clear. Even spokesmen shied away from making definitive judgements lest their evaluations be premature. Dr. Gallaudet, in reviewing its history, was vague about The Literary's role in postwar culture and found it impossible to specify what its importance had been. Nonetheless, he was certain that in an indescribable way Washington was a better place because of its existence—if for no other reason than because it kept the process of establishing intellectual organizations moving steadily along.[56] As its first quarter century drew to a close Ainsworth Spofford stated as unequivocally as he was able: "We count not ourselves as having attained great or noteworthy results, but we are on the road."[57]

Others, more impatient with tentative accomplishments, showed less satisfaction and less optimism. Instead of being buoyed by the worthwhile contributions of members they were dismayed by the mixed quality of programs; rather than having confidence that The Literary would eventually emerge as the embodiment of recognized achievement they tended to ask whether it was degenerating into another version of hothouse culture. In short, there were doubts that, given its direction, the Literary Society could become an elitist association of intellectual merit. Garrick Mallery, for one, urged the elimination of science, poetry, and music from the programs. The former might better be left to Washington's scientific societies, while the poetry and music produced by The Literary were hopelessly second rate. Verses like "Reading to Grandmamma," and tunes such as "Sally in Our Alley" and "Charlie is My Darlin'" failed to convey the desired impression of creativity.[58] More than once Garfield criticized the banality of lectures and discussions, betraying disappointment in The Literary's lack of progress.[59] As early as 1877 Mme. de Hegermann-Lindencrone inferred that it was in eclipse. With sarcastic humor she caricatured the Literary Society as the "enchanted circle of the Brain Club," and recounted the discussion of a paper on "The Metamorphosis of Negative Matter." The beautiful Lillie was an acclaimed vocalist, and at a subsequent meeting Mrs. Dahlgren requested her to sing "Tender and True," a melancholy ballad relating the death of a young soldier who had gone into battle with a memento from his love, a ribbon of blue, pinned over his heart. The composer, Jennie Lincoln, happened to be present, and capped the performance—in a proper Victorian manner—by fainting dead away. Like Mrs. Lincoln, the Literary Society appeared to be on the wane.[60]

It was true that The Literary was fast falling out of date so far as its own taste in letters was concerned. At a time when realism and naturalism were vying to become the dominant genre, members still inclined toward prose that oozed sentimentality. To end the 1889 season there was a general discussion of Realism in Fiction, which turned into a castigation of Zola and an affirmation of the enobling duties of the writer.[61] Despite the call by leading craftsmen for depictions of life with straight-forward frankness, the innocents of The Literary remained entranced by romantic homelies. "A Sentimental Journey," "What is the Deepest Grief?" and "Where Duty Calls," a melodramatic tale about a girl in the country who despaired of ever performing a heroic deed until she suddenly had the opportunity to save two children from a flaming farmhouse were typical products of literary exercises.[62] As one of the founders observed, his Society was partial to "stories of pathetic mould that leave the eyelids wet."[63] The influence of feminine custodians of culture—the very types who launched The Literary—obviously pervaded its activities throughout the nineteenth century. Moreover, it is apparent that during an epochal period of change in literary conventions, the Washington group was becoming *passe*.

In spite of its slightly enfeebled and somewhat retrograde state, The Literary could claim certain successes. First of all it provided an outlet for Washingtonians more interested in written expression than science. By 1874 the ground was already being prepared for a harvest of local scientific associations. No literary organization worthy of the name, except that of Horatio King, graced Washington and members of the Literary Society questioned whether King's reunions did justice to the cause of whetting appetites for polite letters. In order to generate interest was it not necessary to offer opportunities for actual writing and criticism? A circle of luminaries gathered for discussion was important, they agreed, but so too was a coterie of persons who were themselves active contributors.

Both groups selected members with great care, but while King considered social rank of prime importance (it might be argued that his programs were merely excuses for holding reunions), The Literary's founders thought first in terms of encouraging regular participation. Moreover, in light of the reunions' indefinite character, what guaranteed that they would not enter the grave with their sponsor? Thus the Literary Society served a twofold need: it offered greater permanence than King's group, and gave more chance to those who seriously wanted to try their hands at composition.

Aiming at excellence and falling short of the mark was another common characteristic. Both gatherings were more celebrated for social elegance than artistic accomplishment, for enabling Washingtonians to assume the mantle of cultivation rather than denoting real intellectual ferment. The Literary, however, was definitely a cut above King's circle. Its membership rolls contained a catalogue of Washington's scientific community, men who were building national scientific institutions and at the same time establishing local societies for the promotion of their disciplines. The Literary cooperated with organizations that were primarily scientific, and in that way contributed to the general strengthening of intellectual associations, and to the consolidation of individuals sharing like interests and talents. Finally compared with King's reunions, there was its broader cultural influence, which though amorphous was deeply felt. Refreshingly different from the frivolity of dancing parties and reception crushes the Literary Society brightened the local atmosphere. Here, then, was the culmination of Mrs. Dahlgren's crusade to have The Literary cast a "radiance over the conventional inanity of social life in Washington."[64] In this respect it had an "influence which was healthful in the highest degree," but which was as hard to delinate as an invigorating breath of fresh air.[65]

NOTES TO CHAPTER 2

1. For insights into the exalted image of science and the way social benefits accrued from it, see Philip Jerome Borden, "Rite Words in Rote Order: Rankean History in America, 1870-1900" (unpublished Ph.D. dissertation, Department of History, Wayne State University, 1968), pp. 79-81; Daniel J. Kevles, "The Study of Physics in America, 1865-1916" (unpublished Ph.D. dissertation, Department of History, Princeton University, 1964), pp. 22-25, 35-46.

2. Otis T. Mason to Franz Boas, December 3, 1887, Boas Papers, American Philosophical Society; Joseph Henry had said much the same thing seventeen years before in "Examination of Professor Henry by the English Government Scientific Commission," *Smithsonian Miscellaneous Collections,* XVIII (Washington, D. C., 1880), 781-782.

3. L. de Hegermann-Lindencrone, *The Sunny Side of Diplomatic Life, 1875-1912* (New York, 1914), p. 16; for a sketch of Mme. de Hegermann-Lindencrone see Maurice Francis Egan, *Recollections of a Happy Life* (New York, 1924), pp. 63-64; "Washington Gossip," *Cincinnati Commercial,* January 28, 1877, xeroxed copy in the Rutherford B. Hayes Library (henceforth RBHL).

4. Vincent P. DeSantis, "President Garfield and the Solid South," *North Carolina Historical Review,* XXXVI (October, 1959), 446; Vincent P. DeSantis, *Republicans Face the Southern Question: The New Departure Years, 1877-1897* (Baltimore, Md., 1959), p. 109.

5. Hegermann-Lindencrone, *Sunny Side,* pp. 71, 78.

6. For a biographical account by his son see Horatio King, *Turning on the Light...* (Philadelphia, 1895), pp. 7-21.

7. Unsigned letter to Horatio King, December 15, 1870, and King to Henry A. Brewster, January 12, 1871, Horatio King Papers, V, Manuscript Division, Library of Congress (henceforth LC).

8. Horatio King to W. W. Belknap, March 22, 1870, *ibid.*

9. Marian Gouverneur, *As I Remember: Recollections of American Society During the Nineteenth Century* (New York, 1911), p. 377.

10 Horatio King to W. W. Belknap, March 22, 1870, King Papers, V, LC.

11. Horatio King to Frederick T. Dent, February 18, 1870, *ibid.*

12. Horatio King to William K. Rogers, January 11, 1878, Rogers Papers, RBHL.

13. For King's abhorrence of partisanship in literature see Horatio King to Ward H. Lamon, December 5, 1887, Lamon Papers, LN 369, Henry E. Huntington Library and Art Gallery (henceforth HEHL).

14. King's poem to Justin Morrill, April 14, 1885, King Papers, VIII, LC. During the next few years King became the self-appointed "poet-laureate, in MOR-RILL sense," and his verse in honor of the senator's eighty-second birthday is reprinted in King, *Turning on the Light*, pp. 19-30.

15. James Buchanan to Horatio King, June 23, 1866, King Papers, IV, LC.

16. Maria A. Stetson to Horatio King, April 3, 1870, and John S. Cunningham to Horatio King, March 21, 1872, *ibid.*, V.

17. Horatio King to William K. Rogers, January 11, 1878, Rogers Papers, RBHL.

18. Horatio King to W. W. Belknap, March 22, 1870, King Papers, V, LC.

19. Horatio King to William K. Rogers, January 11, 1878, Rogers Papers, RBHL.

20. M. E. N. Howells to Horatio King, January 12, 1871, King Papers, V, LC.

21. Joseph S. Wilson to Horatio King, January 20, 1872, and James A. Ekin to Horatio King, January 16, 1875, *ibid.*, V and VI.

22. Edmund Wilson, *Patriotic Gore: Studies in the Literature of the American Civil War* (New York, 1962), pp. 635-669.

23. Knox Circular Letter, January 16 and March 9, 1880, V, New-York Historical Society.

24. Mrs. William Chapin Huntington has recounted how she was first instructed that "no one, 'no one who is anyone', calls it anything but 'The Literary,'" "Ladies of the Literary," read before the Literary Society of Washington, January 9, 1965, Literary Society of Washington Papers, Manuscript Division, Library of Congress (henceforth Literary Society Papers, LC); see also the account of the five hundredth meeting in *The Washington Herald*, March 28, 1927, p. 5.

25. Helen Nicolay, *Sixty Years of the Literary Society* (Washington, D. C., 1934), *passim;* Thomas M. Spaulding, *The Literary Society in Peace and War* (Washington, D. C., 1947), pp. 8-10.

26. Glyndon G. Van Deusen, *William Henry Seward* (New York, 1967), pp. 553-562.

27. Mary Clemmer Ames, *A Memorial of Alice and Phoebe Cary, with Some of Their Later Poems* (New York, 1873), pp. 38-39, 60-69.

28. Huntington, "Ladies of The Literary," p. 1, and Julia Ten Eyck McBlair, "The Beginnings of the Literary Society: A Paper Read at its Golden Anniversary, January 12, 1924," Literary Society Papers, LC.

29. Benjamin P. Thomas, *Portrait for Posterity: Lincoln and His Biographers* (New Brunswick, N. J., 1947), pp. 94-131.

30. Helen Nicolay, *Lincoln's Secretary: A Biography of John G. Nicolay* (New York, 1949), *passim;* Horatio King to Ward H. Lamon, December 5, 1887, Lamon Papers, LN 369, HEHL.

31. Edward M. Gallaudet to Mary B. Claflin, December 12, 1881, Claflin Papers, RBHL; see also Edward M. Gallaudet to Theodore F. Dwight, February 1 and November 3, 1881, and George Kennan to Theodore F. Dwight, November 7, 1883, Dwight Papers, Massachusetts Historical Society.

32. I. Edwards Clarke, "The Conditions of Literature in Washington at the Time of the Founding of This Society," read before the Literary Society of Washington, January 21, 1899, Literary Society Papers, LC; copies of the constitution are included in Minutes of the Literary Society of Washington, *ibid.*

33. Minutes of the Literary Society of Washington, I, *passim, ibid.;* lists of members appear throughout the Minutes and in Nicolay, *Sixty Years,* pp. 23-25, and Spaulding, *Literary Society,* pp. 23-37.

34. Frank Luther Mott, *Golden Multitudes: The Story of Best Sellers in the United States* (New York, 1947), pp. 136-137; Helen Waite Papashvily, *All the Happy Endings: A Study of the Domestic Novel in America, the Women Who Wrote It, the Women Who Read It, in the Nineteenth Century* (New York, 1956), pp. 110-121, 180-182.

35. Minutes of the Literary Society of Washington, I and II, *passim,* LC.; George Kennan's remarkable career is interestingly summarized by his distant relative,

George Frost Kennan, in the abridged edition of the former's *Siberia and the Exile System* (New York, 1891; University of Chicago Press edn., 1958), pp. ix-xix.

36. Diary of James A. Garfield, December 11, 1875, Garfield Papers, IV, Box 2, LC; *A Tribute of Respect from the Literary Society of Washington to its Late President James Abram Garfield* (Washington, D. C., 1882), *passim*.

37. Diary of Edward M. Gallaudet, March 12, 1881, Gallaudet Papers, LC.

38. "Washington Gossip," *Cincinnati Commercial*, December 24, 1876, xeroxed copy in RBHL.

39. Lloyd Lewis and Henry Justin Smith, *Oscar Wilde Discovers America* (New York, 1936), pp. 83-90.

40. Minutes of the Literary Society of Washington, I and II, *passim*, LC.

41. Both MSS and published lectures are contained in boxes labeled "Various Publications," and "Some Papers Presented at Meetings," Literary Society Papers, LC.

42. Minutes of the Executive Committee, December 11, 1876, *ibid*.

43. Minutes of the Literary Society of Washington, I and II, *passim*, *ibid*.

44. Ainsworth R. Spofford, unpublished comments on the twenty-fifth anniversary of the Literary Society of Washington, January 21, 1899, box labeled "Documents Relating to the History of the Society," *ibid*.

45. Madeleine V. Dahlgren, "Statement of the Purposes of the Literary Society of Washington" (1888), *ibid.*, Box 5.

46. Madeleine Vinton Dahlgren to Editor Youth Companion [M. A. Dewolfe Howe], January 9, 1889, Howe Papers, Houghton Library, Harvard University.

47. Henry James, *Pandora* (1884), *The Novels and Tales of Henry James* (New York, 1909), XVIII, 145.

48. Christopher C. Cox, "To the Members of the 'Dahlgren Literary Society,' " Literary Society Papers, LC, Box 5; for Mrs. Dahlgren's influence in The Literary's affairs see Madeleine V. Dahlgren to Spencer F. Baird, December 3, 1878, Spencer F. Baird Personal Papers, Smithsonian Institution Archives;

Florence P. Spofford to Nevin M. Fenneman, January 29, 1923, box labeled "Documents Relating to the History of the Society," and Huntington, "Ladies of The Literary," p. 2, Literary Society Papers, LC.

49. Minutes of the Literary Society of Washington, March 26, 1881, and January 15, 1881, and March 24, 1888, *ibid.*, I.

50. *Ibid.*, May 13, 1882.

51. *Ibid.*, February 22, 1890, II.

52. *Ibid.*, January 25, 1890.

53. *Ibid.*, December 11, 1880, I.

54. Olive Risley Seward's statement of the purpose of the Literary Society, *ibid.*, Box 5.

55. Madeleine V. Dahlgren, "Statement of the Purposes of the Literary Society," *ibid.*

56. "Dr. Gallaudet's Remarks," undated, box labeled "Some Papers Presented at Meetings," *ibid.*

57. Ainsworth R. Spofford, unpublished comments on the twenty-fifth anniversary of the Literary Society of Washington, January 21, 1899, box labeled "Documents Relating to the History of the Society," *ibid.*

58. Minutes of the Literary Society of Washington, February 24, 1888, *ibid.*, I.

59. Diary of James A. Garfield, January 10, and April 3, 1880, Garfield Papers, IX, Box 5, LC.

60. de Hegermmann-Lindencrone, *Sunny Side*, p. 16; Egan, *Recollections*, p. 64.

61. Minutes of the Literary Society of Washington, May 4, 1889, I, Literary Society Papers, LC; The Literary was not unique in spurning realism at this time, as is shown by Warner Berthoff, *The Ferment of Realism: American Literature, 1884-1919* (New York, 1965).

62. Minutes of the Literary Society of Washington, January 15, 1889, I, Literary Society Papers, LC.

63. Christopher C. Cox, "To the Members of the 'Dahlgren Literary Society,' " *ibid*, Box 5.

64. Madeleine V. Dahlgren to Carl Schurz, December [1878?] , Schurz Papers, XLVII, General Correspondence, LC.

65. "Dr. Gallaudet's Remarks," undated, box labeled "Some Papers Presented at Meetings," Literary Society Papers, LC.

3

Of A Strictly Scientific Character

"The art of destroying life," observed Joseph Henry during the grim winter of 1862-63, "as well as that of preserving it, calls for the application of scientific principles, and the institution of scientific experiments on a scale of magnitude which would never be attempted in time of peace."[1] Henry was suggesting that a positive result of the Civil War would be its influence in advancing American science. His wish went unfulfilled, however, and the statement must be read as an exaggeration of the role of science in the Union war effort.

Henry, himself, admitted as much in 1870 in response to questions from members of the English Government Scientific Commission. The Commission had been appointed to study means for improving scientific education and research, and while vacationing in London, Henry agreed to testify on how science was supported in the United States. There was little he could tell his British peers—aside from calling attention to ways the Smithsonian went about increasing and diffusing knowledge among men—since at that time the development of science in the United States happened to be relatively stagnant. Annual appropriations by the states and Congress totaled a paltry half-million dollars, which was divided among the United States Coast Survey, the Naval Observatory, lighthouse experimentation and various western reconnaissance groups. No sums were spent for scientific scholarships or original investigations. Scientific societies, including the National Academy, received nothing from the government, and consequently had little voice in matters of public policy.[2]

Contemporaries traced official Washington's neglect of science to the alleged American indifference toward basic research. This condition was noted by Henry and deplored unsparingly by Simon Newcomb, who rated America's contribution to "exact science" at "nearly zero," attributing its glaring failure to defects of national character.

"It is an unpopular truth that in every department of exact thought America is a generation behind the age," he told Charles Eliot Norton in 1868. In contrast to other nations in which there were traditions of "sufficient inducement to make young men of the highest talents engage in scientific pursuits," in America the advancement of abstract knowledge had been seriously retarded by the crippling tendency to downgrade pure intellectual curiosity. Practicality, utility, and common sense were celebrated instead.[3] Understandably, to Newcomb the government had no cause to encourage basic science or to utilize the country's finest scientific minds.[4]

Newcomb's interpretation was determined by his absorption in the physical sciences and his dubious comparisons of the United States and Europe.[5] Another assessment of science in the seventies was far more positive, and interestingly its perspective on the American scene came not from Europe, but from the Far East. At just about the time Henry was visiting England, and Newcomb was preparing his *North American Review* articles, Arinori Mori came to Washington as Japan's chargé d'affaires. Mori's reputation stemmed largely from his *Life and Resources in America,* published in 1871. His astute observations gained him the image of a Japanese Tocqueville. James Garfield spoke for the Washington establishment in pronouncing him "a very intelligent and even remarkable man."[6] Mori's assertion, that "there is scarcely any country in which original talents, applied to pure scientific investigation, meets with less reward," was hardly an observation of genius. But Mori did perceive "a growing inclination on the part of the government and of wealthy individuals to endow establishments for the advance of pure science." He recognized too that undertakings begun for the sake of practical utility could end up contributing to abstract knowledge.[7] The Civil War effected none of this, however, and in Mori's optimistic survey of science in America it was as if the War had never happened.

Indeed, it can be argued that the immediate impact of the Civil War on science was negligible. Neither side claimed a weapons technology sufficiently advanced to threaten the other. No armaments were developed that required research in the exact sciences. Most innovations came from the hands of amateur inventors rather than from the trained minds of chemists and physicists. There was never much consideration given to mobilizing professional scientists in order to take advantage of their expertise. Practical individuals blessed with mechanical intuition were what the country needed, it was felt, not true savants. The latter were in short supply anyway, a fact helping to explain why they were generally ignored by the government.

Physical science had not yet reached the stage at which it could be exploited for purposes of mass annihilation; industrial research was not adequately developed to yield instruments of destruction; and, of course, universities were still decades away from being sucked into the war machine. Therefore, the country was without the necessary ingredients for waging a scientific war. Between 1861 and 1865 the National Academy of Sciences and the Permanent Commission instituted to advise the Navy Department on scientific matters accomplished little. Even the attempts of the National Academy to ascertain the age of whiskey administered in hospitals proved a failure. Such shortcomings and disappointments have led to the conclusion that, "During the Civil War, the nearest thing to a research and development agency was the President himself."[8]

Though the military experience of the war years failed to hasten scientific progress appreciably, the middle period of American history was a vital one in terms of organization and professionalization. As early as 1840 a lively interest was shown in every branch of science, and this enthusiasm led to and resulted from scientific institutions which multiplied at a rapid pace. Between 1842 and 1848, the Navy's Depot of Charts and Instruments was transformed into the Naval Observatory. The Coast Survey was revitalized under the direction of Benjamin Franklin's shrewd and capable great grandson, Alexander Dallas Bache. The Smithsonian Institution was founded to be a future national center for science. Benjamin Silliman improved his *American Journal of Science and Arts,* the principal organ for scientific publication in the United States. New observatories, museums, and laboratories were built at Cincinnati, Williams College, Yale, and Harvard. Harvard University's Lawrence Scientific School opened its doors. The American Association for the Advancement of Science was born, and vigorous societies and academies of science flourished in many southern cities. All the while various public and private agencies were dispatching research parties which unearthed vast quantities of specimens and data, published numerous reports, and also helped educate the scientists themselves. Simultaneously, scientists were being more amply rewarded with money and status. Despite the federal government's hesitancy about encouraging learning, the middle 1840's constituted a watershed in the development of science in America.[9] The Civil War could not have brought maturation for that had already occurred. Just as other areas of national culture experienced antebellum "take-off" periods, so did American science. This impetus was sustained until the Gilded Age.

Late nineteenth century America witnessed another epoch of ferment and acceleration. Though the term "scientist" was first used in the 1840's,[10] it did not warrant meaningful application until after the Civil War when science inexorably emerged as a vocation and a profession. "The sun of science now rides high in heaven, and floods the earth with hot and dusty light," observed geologist J. P. Lesley in 1885. "What was once play has turned to serious toil . . . . The few and early risers have become a multitude."[11] This "multitude" of full-time scientists showed an ever increasing number whose orientation was professional; individuals who had received specialized academic training and who functioned through the regularized institutions, journals, and associations established by their subdisciplines. Some held faculty appointments in colleges and universities, others were employed by observatories, while many more enjoyed the patronage of state and federal governments.[12]

Clarence Edward Dutton recalled the seventies as a time when "all of those great bureaus for scientific investigation under governmental auspices and support, which are such conspicuous features of our system, were then in existence and in full career. . ."[13] Major Dutton knew whereof he spoke. His own analyses of rock formations and vivid, panoramic descriptions of the high plateaus of Utah and Grand Canyon country were made possible by more than fifteen years service with the Powell Survey, the Public Lands Comission, the United States Geological Survey, and the Irrigation Survey. Dutton's experience provided a personal illustration of scientific activity under the aegis of the government. It was doubly interesting because he was drawn into public service mainly through his affiliation with one of the scientific community's notable organizations, the Philosophical Society of Washington. Members of the Philosophical Society helped nurture his geological speculations, and the contacts which it afforded enabled him to pursue a long career in government agencies.[14]

While not officially founded until 1871, the Philosophical Society's roots ran back to the Scientific Club of the 1850's. This continuity between post and antebellum scientific institutions was highlighted by the figure of Joseph Henry as a leading organizer of both groups. That Henry should have been conspicuously in the forefront in 1871 was at once understandable and appropriate. He had just returned from his exchange with the English Commission, during which the inadequacy of America's scientific establishment had been so forcefully brought home. Organizing the Philosophical Society was therefore a calculated response to this challenging realization. In another way Henry's presence seemed fitting as he was already the center of Washington's most learned circle, a group which styled itself the Scientific Club.

The designation "club" should not be taken too literally, however, since this body was never as tightly organized as the term implies. It lacked even the most rudimentary element of a club: a roster of regular members. There was a good deal of vagueness about the name, with some calling it "The Saturday Club" and Spencer Baird referring to it simply as "The Washington Scientifics." This ill-defined coterie took its existence from the custom of Henry and his friends passing Saturday evenings in each others' company.

Commencing early in the 1850's, these pleasant gatherings were held "for the discussion of scientific subjects and for general scientific conversation,"[15] aims which, in practice, proved broad enough to encompass disparate specialities. Hugh McCulloch learned this upon coming to Washington as comptroller of the currency. Shortly after arriving he received an invitation from the Scientific Club, which he refused, apologizing that he was poorly versed in science. No matter, insisted Henry, "finance is a subject in which the country is just now deeply interested, and the Club wants a member who knows something about it."[16]

McCulloch soon became a steady visitor, along with others whose fields lay outside of pure science. Several had positions in the Patent Office, including Titian Peale, explorer, artist, mechanic, photographer, and naturalist—a fascinating product of one of the country's most singular families. Quartermaster General Montgomery C. Meigs, George Schaeffer, librarian of the Interior Department, and Major General Andrew Atkinson Humphreys, chief of the army Corps of Engineers augmented a nucleus of mathematicians, geodesists, astronomers, and physicists. These men would assemble at one of their number's residence, hear a paper, then close the evening with supper. Since Henry was an ever willing host, meetings frequently took place at the Smithsonian. Those occasions left particularly vivid impressions in the minds of participants because the professor used his scientific knowledge to concoct a punch with a base of pure alcohol. Intellectual offerings were equally imaginative, and well-deserved was the accolade that the meetings were "the highest possible example of social life at the Nation's capital."[17]

The fatal flaw of the Scientific Club was a lack of institutional structure. Unlike most elegant circles all its members were "gentlemen of superior culture," and it justifiably took precedence over groups like Horatio King's.[18] In no sense was it a haven for mere *aficionados* of the arts and sciences, but instead an elitist body of specialists and professionals. A revealing aspect of its history was the absence of any talk about merging with the Washington Scientific Association, a collection of buffs which had little in common with the Scientific Club aside from its name.[19] Saturday get togethers were looked forward to with such expectation that men would venture out on the most bitter and blustery January night rather than forfeit the warm fellowship of the Scientific Club. But for all that, Henry's group was not well organized, a problem which became acute with the enlargement of Washington's scientific corps during the late 1860's. By 1871 attendance at meetings was running as high as fifty. Clearly the Scientific Club had outgrown its casual character and the time was ripe for a more comprehensive organization. Before the first quarter of the new year had run its course it would be formalized into the Philosophical Society of Washington.[20]

Responding to the plea of forty-three Washingtonians interested in scientific pursuits, Joseph Henry called a meeting for the purpose of creating a society which would satisfy the needs of local savants. Benjamin Peirce, Asaph Hall, Steven Vincent Benet, General Sherman, Salmon P. Chase, Peale, Meigs, Schaeffer, Humphreys, and Newcomb totaled a small percentage of those who affirmed their commitment to the ideal of an organization "having for its object the free exchange of views and studies on scientific subjects, and the promotion of scientific inquiry among its members." On March 13th, in the Smithsonian Regent's Room, they adopted a constitution and elected officers. Henry was chosen the first president of the Society, and its constitution and bylaws were formally ratified on April 1st. Almost overnight professional ties among the Capital City's men of specialized knowledge were strengthened. More definite form had been given to the constellation of resident intellectuals, and the seat of government was now illuminated by "a society for the *advancement* of science."[21]

Given the Society's focus of attention, would it not have been appropriate to retain the title and idea of the Scientific Club? Here was "an association of a strictly scientific character."[22] Why then give up a name which seemed perfectly suitable? The answer lay in the founders' belief that all "those branches of knowledge that relate to the positive facts and laws of the physical and moral universe" touch the essence of science. Because the men involved were concerned with truth and wisdom in the fullest sense, they chose to describe themselves as "Philosophical." They had not united for relaxation or amusement, but to stimulate their joint quest for empirical understanding. The founders therefore parted company with Henry's circle, and in the process "Club" was replaced by "Society." Societies had always generated much of the energy for scientific progress. This committment could be sustained Henry advised, by the corporate sharing of new discoveries, by improving the image of American science, and by influencing popular thought.

> However wide the diffusion of general knowledge, public opinion in regard to scientific questions must eventually be determined by the authority of societies, journals, and individuals, of established scientific reputation. It is therefore of the first importance that the operations of this Society be conducted with great care, and that nothing be given to the world under its sanction which is not based upon thorough investigation or established scientific principles.[23]

The Philosophical Society regarded itself as more than a clique of hometown scientists. According to Henry it aspired to help chart the course of national development, an immense challenge to say the least.

Naturally, much depended on the caliber of the membership. At the very outset it was made clear that those who might fail to pass muster need not apply. "While but comparatively few qualifications are necessary for admittance," Henry explained, "no person is elected who is not supposed to have at least a high appreciation of science; has some familiarity with its principles, and is capable of doing something in the way of promoting the objects of the Association."[24] The latter might entail just making a "good audience"—assuming, of course, that the candidate met the criterion of "general culture"—but on no account would the Society accept "pseudo-scientists."[25] Taking only relatively trained minds vouchsafed the Society's position with regard to the elegant circles. These aggregations were well intentioned and worthwhile, in so far as they encouraged self-improvement, but the national capital was both deserving and capable of better. Washington already claimed proportionately more individuals engaged in scientifically oriented pursuits than any other city, and with the predicted growth of government science this number was bound to multiply. Before long the Society would revolve around original investigators collectively comparing and testing aspects of their research. By attracting the superior talent of national institutions, the Philosophical Society would simultaneously nourish the spirit of inquiry in Washington and "have reflex influence upon every part of the United States."[26]

The standards set for meetings were still more rigorous than those pertaining to membership. Since the Society assumed responsibility for scrutinizing claims to advances in knowledge its proceedings were conducted with utmost seriousness. In this vein evening dress was *de rigueur* for participants, thereby imparting an aura of formal dignity. Twice a month between twenty and thirty members convened to hear and comment upon prepared papers. These contributions were almost invariably of a high order, and remarks from the audience that hinted of pedestrianism were coldly received. "Free critical discussion," as Henry understood it, was meant to be constructive, calling attention to neglected facts, clarifying hypotheses, and refining tentative conclusions. Informed criticism was therefore an indispensible part of the Society's operations. Although in the beginning most lectures dealt with pure science, the scope of the Society's interest included "Dreams in Their Relation to Psychology," a talk on the Brooklyn Bridge, William H. Dall's "On the Relative Value of Alaska to the United States," "An Attempt at a Theory of Odor," a travelogue of the Middle East by General Sherman, C. E. Dutton's treatment of the silver question, and J. H. Saville, "On the New Japanese Coinage." An unforgettable evening was when Professor Alexander Graham Bell gave an early public demonstration of his telephone. Significantly, the papers presented at the Society's meetings appeared in mass circulation periodicals as well as lesser known scholarly journals. Cultivated readers of *Scribner's* or *Harper's New Monthly Magazine*, and those who poured over *Annals of the Harvard College Observatory* and the *Annual Report of the U.S. Fish Commission*, were equally apt to be treated to a Philosophical Society paper. In either case they were bound to be impressed by the competence of the author and the self-evident earnestness of his organization. [27]

Yet conviviality also had a place in the Society's existence, as illustrated by the tradition of "adjourned meetings." Regular meetings were held fortnightly in the old Ford's Theatre. After Lincoln's assassination the building had been turned into an annex of the Surgeon General's office to house the Army Medical Museum and Library with Dr. John Shaw Billings in charge.

By happy coincidence Billings, and Surgeon General J. K. Barnes, happened to be founders of the Philosophical Society. Through their official capacities they arranged for the Society's first home. Between 1871 and 1887, until the Cosmos Club auditorium was available, the narrow stairs of Ford's Theatre were ascended countless times as members made their way to the dingy, "rather gloomy" room which Dr. Billings found nonetheless "appropriate to the objects and purposes of the company gathered therein." [28] Perhaps this somber ambience contributed to the main order of business, but it also seems to have prepared members for their retirement immediately afterward to a tavern around the corner for beer, pretzels, and oysters. Philosophical Society evenings always concluded by moving from the gray of theory into the green of life. The policy of postponing refreshments may have reflected apprehension over the tarnished image of the Megatherium Club, an organization of Washington naturalists in the late 1850's which was rumored to harbor dissipates. Of greater import was the way adjourned meetings carried on the Henry tradition of trying to blend sociability with intellectual pursuits.[29]

A novelty without precedent in the Scientific Club was a publication of minutes. The *Bulletin of the Philosophical Society of Washington,* printed by the Smithsonian, first appeared in 1874. Somewhat sporadically, during the next seventeen years, ten more volumes containing resumes of as few as one and as many as four years of meetings were made available. Each volume contained a list of officers and members, the constitution and rules. But out of economic necessity scientific journals, government documents, and the Smithsonian Institution's *Miscellaneous Collections* (the secretary of the Smithsonian occupied a permanent place on the publications committee) had to be relied on for the distribution of complete papers.[30] Before 1888 just titles and abstracts of communications were presented, with only the president's annual address given in full. Consequently, the early *Bulletin* revealed but an outline of the Society's substance.

Nonetheless, this represented a breakthrough for both the Society and the promotion of Washington science. Virtually any record of proceedings served to differentiate between truly dynamic organizations and elegant circles. "Without at least such a publication," warned Henry, "the society cannot have a recognized existence."[31]

The *Bulletin* met a publish-or-perish demand by partially filling the needs of individual members for an outlet, while at the same time giving an impression of organizational vitality. Henry had always maintained that one of the most effective means for advancing science was by regularly disseminating notices of accretions to knowledge. Such a task was beyond the range of the Scientific Club, but the more elaborate machinery of the Philosophical Society made this possible. As president, Henry deplored the delay in producing the first volume, and the *Bulletin* never satisfied his hopes for a comprehensive series of transactions. Not until ten years after his death was the publication policy revised to permit the printing of entire articles. Yet a delinquent journal of limited scope was preferable to nothing at all. By 1879, when it began a regular yearly schedule, the *Bulletin* was received by major libraries and research institutions throughout North America and Europe. Exchanges had been established with over a dozen royal societies and imperial academies, and to an increasing extent the Philosophical Society of Washington was emerging as a leading spokesman for national science.

It was Joseph Henry's custom to begin meetings by reading from a volume of Royal Society *Transactions,* from which might be inferred comparability with the older British institution.[32] Both groups were founded, in the main, by mathematicians, astronomers, and physical scientists. The mid-seventeenth century circle at London and the Scientific Club in antebellum Washington were somewhat similar. Although each accepted members from outside the ranks of professional science and avoided rigid specialization, each stressed enlightened discussion, and gradually grew more formal, national, and influential.

During the nineteenth century the growth of elitist clubs and societies occurred in both England and America against backgrounds that were unmistakably similar. The English experience was colored by the aftermath of the Napoleonic Wars. Rapid social and economic changes reverberating throughout the class system, and the general condition of cultural disorder combined to produce "the great age of the London club."[33] As in America somewhat later a protracted military effort brought about a concentration in the national capital of scientists and talented civil servants. These men of common interests sought opportunities for association like those already enjoyed by aristocrats and politicians. Though they surfaced in the wake of heightened nationalism the new intellectual groups were not notably nationalistic. On the contrary, they often served as meeting places for foreign scientists and men of letters. As President Asaph Hall reminded the Philosophical Society: "Let us welcome all earnest men, remembering that the principles of science are universal, and are not confined to any language or country."[34] Finally, there were striking parallels in composition and character. The London Athenaeum, for instance, was established for eminences in the arts and sciences, a genuine intellectual elite.[35] Certainly, the Philosophical Society of Washington approximated this status as it came to include more and more men of national distinction.

Undergirding this rise to prominence was a hierarchial structure designed to take utmost advantage of the prestige of individual members. The Philosophical Society was created as an elite organization, and those in charge studiously made certain that it would be identified with the cream of official Washington. "It is not a public establishment," wrote Henry, "and is composed of members and such persons as are especially invited."[36] Moreover, its leaders and its most famous personages were one and the same, guaranteeing that brilliant exhibits would constantly appear. Henry, who also was president of the National Academy, held the Society's highest office every year until his death, when it devolved to the second ranking member, Simon Newcomb. Likewise, Baird, General Humphreys, Meigs, Julius Hilgard, J. J. Woodward, Abbe, Asaph Hall, Charles Schott, Thomas L. Casey, Gill, and J. H. C. Coffin—all in the National Academy—were so often returned to office that their names became synonymous with the Society itself.

The tactic of building a reputation around illustrious figures had been profitably employed by other groups as well. However, in contrast to the majority of exquisite circles the Society's ornaments not only dazzled, they also governed. As stipulated in the constitution and standing rules, the executive officers and nine-man general committee transacted all business independent of the rest of the membership. Meeting separately, prior to the regular sessions, they passed judgement on communications, considered amendments to the bylaws, set financial policies, and even decided upon membership nominations. "For the government of men whose object is the advance of *truth,* but few rules are necessary," assured the president upon introducing his Society to the public. Elitist rule brought operational efficiency, and the "devotion of almost every evening exclusively to its legitimate purposes."[37] This brand of authoritarianism followed from Henry's belief that federal office holders should have longer terms, and that the president might serve for life.[38] With regard to his own Society, it enabled the star performers to choose supporting casts that were consonant with the character and purposes of their organization.

Certain members took exception to these elitist configurations. In May of 1883, just two months after his admission, Albert Williams privately deprecated it as "the Washington Mutual Admiration Society" and described the lectures as "slush."[39] Since Williams occupied one of the fashionable residences on Lafayette Square and was employed by the United States Geological Survey, this low opinion of a group patently well tailored to his own position seemed to defy reason. Some light was shed by the confidential report of a colleague, Samuel Franklin Emmons, after addressing the Society.

I wish I was a little better up in Chemistry and Physics myself, but don't seem to have time to do any studying on so abstract a line as that . . . . The paper of which you heard . . . I wrote out at [Grove Karl] Gilbert's request for the Washington Philosophical Society. He told me they were a lot of old fogies to whom anything of that kind would be a novelty. I therefore took very little pains about it, and merely read the paper and sent in a hurried abstract . . . .[40]

Emmons's sarcasm lifted the veil which hid the professional jealousies among Washington's men of science. As geologists, Williams, Emmons, and Gilbert resented the denigration of their specialties by physical scientists and the minority status of natural science in the Philosophical Society. Had not their former president, Simon Newcomb, disparaged them in his *North American Review* articles a few short years before?[41] What meaning could be attached to the Society's establishment of a mathematical section during the previous month, other than that it signalled the absolute hegemony of exact science? Actually there was no such juggernaut of physicists, astronomers, and mathematicians (at times the mathematical section would not meet for months on end). Natural scientists lectured often, and in 1883, while the three geologists were sharing their dissatisfactions, the president was John Wesley Powell.

By sniping at "old fogies," Emmons and Gilbert demonstrated the potential for serious antagonisms within the Society. This term, or something close to it, had traditionally been used to stigmatize those who threatened to tarnish the image of science and who endangered professional development. It derived from the great fear of "charlatanism," which in 1838 caused Joseph Henry to warn that "we must put down quackery or quackery will put down science."[42] It was a particular peril to institution-builders such as Louis Agassiz, who in 1863 insisted that the initial business of the National Academy of Sciences "should be to remedy the infirmity of the first appointments by submitting the whole again to a vote and making arrangements by which old fogies could be dropped from time to time, so that the Academy shall always be a live body."[43] The charge was sometimes misdirected, as in the case of Emmons and Gilbert in 1883. Their "old fogies" were in reality symbols, just as Williams's "slush" had less to do with Society papers than with work performed in other branches. Similarly, their implied contempt for the elitist control of the Society actually applied to the status accorded abstract science, "that profound respect which pertains to comparative ignorance . . . ."[44] Their concern with "old fogeyism" may have been overdrawn. Nonetheless, it sounded a dissonant note in the affairs of the Society.

The pique of disgruntled members also revealed a basic contradiction in the Society. Its paramount objective was the advancement of science, but at the same time it sought to operate informally as a social club. These ends were mutually incompatible; professional prejudice and distrust were too strong among government scientists to permit a comprehensive organization of genuine fellowship and good will. Either it could, in a serious fashion, promote national science and forget about sociability, or it might disregard substantive matters and thereby increase the chances for developing a pleasant milieu. This dilemma was not of the Society's making, but inadvertently the Society institutionalized it. Encompassing disparate groups of professionals assured the exaccerbation of existing rivalries, and thrashing out issues upon which men had already taken intellectual positions lengthened the odds in favor of a factionalized association. No wonder the merriment of adjourned meetings was at times brittle.

Henry considered this to be an innate characteristic of a strictly scientific organization, of "a society for the *advancement* of science" rather than its mere diffusion. The Philosophical Society of Washington, he explained in 1877, "tends to keep alive an active spirit of scientific advancement, not only to diffuse a knowledge of the progress of discovery among its members, but also to stimulate by friendly criticism and cordial sympathy to new efforts in the way of explorations of the unknown."[45] But the objective of "friendly criticism and cordial sympathy" tended to be undermined by tension. The problem was more deep-seated than the inability of members to master personal foibles. The Society reflected the world of American science in microcosm and all its petty antagonisms. Here was the supreme irony: the Society had indeed become an authoritative voice of national science, but in so doing its secondary function was attenuated.

The heart of the matter was that Henry's organization sought to promote science in general, hardly noticing the flow of specialization which periodically threatened to engulf it. This became increasingly frustrating and there was much chafing under the commitment to generalization long after it had had its day. The standing rules seemed to suggest a remedy by sanctioning suborganizations to represent particular branches of science. Accordingly, on March 29, 1883 a separate section was formed for the reading of papers in applied mathematics.[46] but this exhausted the Society's willingness to embrace specialization. Two years later President Asaph Hall, who was also the mathematical chairman, voiced his acceptance of tradition: "Our Society has been established on a broad basis . . . the purpose of a paper should be to present the principle points clearly, and the author may generally trust to the intelligence of his audience to fill in the details."[47]

Echoing his predecessor, John Shaw Billings disapproved of the "polarization" of science and even registered his opposition to the distinctions drawn between different branches, though "there seems to be no way of preventing it."[48] The issue was ignored until G. K. Gilbert observed that the Society was not "adapted to the presentation of highly specialized researches . . . it has discountenanced those papers which from their nature can interest only the devotees of a single science, and it, therefore, has not fully met the needs of the scientific community."[49]

But this did not detract from the Society's significance for American cultural history. Its steadfast encouragement of the generalizing mind exposed a limitation of the emerging technical expert, the "trained man with special abilities in one field" whose narrow margins of comprehension left him incapable of understanding "where, in society, his own skills became mixed with all other knowledge."[50] On another level the Society's founding illustrated the developmental pattern of scientific institutions. After the potent 1840s and 50s, and following the subsequent "period of disorganization," an intellectual elite dedicated to advancing science had taken shape in the national capital.[51] Here was an achievement of the first magnitude. The Philosophical Socity fulfilled a dream which was almost as old as the republic itself. In the early autumn of 1800, Vice-President Jefferson received a letter from Paris written by Joel Barlow. Barlow's brief message brimed with enthusiasm over the promotion of national culture in France and how it might be duplicated at home. Apropos of the French experience, he wrote, there should be established an institution "called the Polysophic Society or some such name," to direct science and learning in the United States, "its members to be chosen for their eminence." Located at "the seat of government in America" its influence would be "national," and its effect upon the "amelioration of society" nothing short of momentous.[52] Little came of Barlow's proposal and over the years his ideal grew dim. It never faded completely, however, due to the vision of men like Henry. And of course it was Henry who redeemed the concept three-quarters of a century later. In the wake of his European trip, with the urgency for learned institutions very much in mind, he saw to it that the nation was provided with a society in Washington for the advancement of science.

So forceful was Henry's leadership that the Society, like the Smithsonian, seemed almost an extension of the professor's mind and spirit. Both institutions manifested his awareness of national potentialities, and under his tutelage each helped to enrich American culture. "The Smithsonian," wrote James Dwight Dana, "is a central finding establishment for the Museums of the country, and whatever helps them helps the science of the whole land."[53] A foreign visitor called it the "one institution in America which promises to exercise a considerable influence on the development of science and of scientific life."[54] Over the years—especially during the latter part of his lifetime—Henry bolstered the Smithsonian through his extensive support of several additional organizations. None, however, matched the Philosophical Society in his conceptions of national progress. On the occasion of his last presidential address, the founding father reiterated that it would above all else, "keep alive an active spirit of scientific advancement." [55] By this time, however, his injunction had less relevance to the future than to an accomplished fact, for the success of his Society was now assured.

After he died Henry's great rule of conduct remained intact. There was no deviating from the first principle of the Society, not even for the sake of creating an atmosphere of greater accommodation. Nor did the Society become much more attuned to specialization. The original order of priorities was maintained, keeping it a Society for the study and promotion of all new contributions to scientific knowledge. As such, members could take pride in the excellent run of diversified lectures and their own "broadening of mental boundaries." [56] Volumes of the *Bulletin* were enlarged by five and six times so that they could carry up to fifteen articles and more illustrations. In 1888 the *Bulletin* ceased to be printed at the Smithsonian's expense. By that time the Society had graduated to self-sufficiency. [57] The Society was on a firm financial footing, having supplemented its income from the $5.00 annual dues with interest on United States, Columbia Railway, and Cosmos Club bonds.

At the end of the century it was decided that because "science and exact knowledge may be cultivated, not only by the reading and discussion of papers explaining the researches carried out by individuals . . . but also by direct agencies tending to promote science where it most needs active work," there was a demand for a committee to apprise members of available grants-in-aid. [58]

The membership by then had increased to about two hundred. Significantly, the additions included many individuals from outside Washington and many promising young men. To a certain degree, however, the Society incorporated rather than diminished professional peevishness. But this was a subordinate purpose anyway; better to realize the primary goal than the one of lesser importance. Even if these ends had not been contradictory they certainly were too much for a single organization to attain. Furthermore a new group had already accepted the challenge of fostering a sense of community among Washington's men of science. From out of the cross-purposes of the Philosophical Society came a different sort of institution to attempt what Henry's failed to achieve. As though foreordained by some compensatory law, the year 1878, when Joseph Henry was laid to rest, also marked the birth of the Cosmos Club.

NOTES TO CHAPTER 3

1. Joseph Henry, "Report of the Secretary," *Annual Report of the Smithsoninan Institution, 1862* (Washington, D. C., 1880), p. 13.

2. [Joseph Henry], "Examination of Professor Henry by the English Government Scientific Commission," *Smithsonian Miscellaneous Collections,* XVIII (Washington, D. C., 1880), 775-801.

3. *Ibid.,* 785; Simon Newcomb, "Exact Science in America," *North American Review,* CXIX (October, 1874), 292, and "Abstract Science in America, 1776-1876," *ibid.,* CXXII (January, 1876), 88-123; a conceptually sounder interpretation is presented in, Richard Harrison Shryock, "American Indifference to Basic Science During the Nineteenth Century," *Archives Interrrnationales d'Histoire des Sciences,* V (Octobre, 1948), 50-65; Simon Newcomb to Charles E. Norton, January 18, 1868, Norton Papers, Houghton Library, Harvard University; a penetrating critique of Shryock and the "indifference literature" is Nathan Reingold's, "American Indifference to Basic Research: A Reappraisal," *Nineteenth Century American Science: A Reappraisal,* ed. George H. Daniels (Evanston, Ill., 1972), pp. 38-62; see also Nathan Reingold, "Alexander Dalles Bache: Science and Technology in the American Idiom," *Technology and Culture,* XI (April, 1970), 176.

4. Simon Newcomb, "Science and the Government," *North American Review,* CLXX (May, 1900), 666-678.

5. Edward Lurie, "An Interpretation of Science in the Nineteenth Century: A Study in History and Historiography," *Journal of World History,* VIII (1965), 685-686.

6. James A. Garfield to Burke A. Hinsdale, January 6, 1873, *Garfield-Hinsdale Letters: Correspondence Between James Abram Garfield and Burke Aaron Hinsdale,* ed. Mary L. Hinsdale (New York, 1969), p. 207; Mori, who was Japan's first diplomatic envoy to the United States (March 1871-March 1873), had initially observed America during his ten-month visit in 1867-68. For a full account of his fascinating career, his effectiveness in heading the Japanese Legation, his popularity and respected position in Washington, his friendship with Joseph Henry, and his *Life and Resources in America* and its probable debt to

Tocqueville's *Democracy in America,* see Ivan Parker Hall, *Mori Arinori* (Cambridge, Mass., 1973), pp. 155-228.

7. Arinori Mori, *Life and Resources in America (Washington, D. C., 1871), pp. 292- 297.*

8. Robert V. Bruce, *Lincoln and the Tools of War* (Indianapolis, Ind., 1956), p. 225; Nathan Reingold, "Science in the Civil War: The Permanent Commission of the Navy Department," *Isis,* XLIX (September, 1958), 307-318; for the Committee on the Question of Tests for the Purity of Whiskey, 1864, see Frederick W. True (ed.), *A History of the First Half-Century of the National Academy of Sciences, 1863-1913* (Washington, D. C., 1913), pp. 225-226.

9. Lurie, "Science in the Nineteenth Century," *Journal of World History,* VIII (1965), 688-695.

10. George H. Daniels, "The Process of Professionalization in American Science: The Emergent Period, 1820-1860," *Isis,* LVIII (Summer, 1967), 154; George H. Daniels, *American Science in the Age of Jackson* (New York, 1968), pp. 38-40.

11. J. P. Lesley, address on retiring from the presidency of the American Association for the Advancemennnt of Science, AAAS *Proceedings,* XXXIV (1885), 1, quoted in, George H. Daniels, "The Pure-Science Ideal and Democratic Culture," *Science,* CLVI (June, 1967), 1701.

12. Daniels states that, "By 1880 there were approximately 400 colleges and universities employing at least one scientist each . . . ." And that, "By the end of the 19th century the American federal government had become the world's greatest supporter of scientific research." *Ibid.,* 1701-1703.

13. Address delivered by Major C. E. Dutton, *The Twenty-Fifth Anniversary of the Founding of the Cosmos Club of Washington, D. C., with a Documentary History of the Club from its Organization to November 16, 1903* (Washington D. C., 1904), p. 25.

14. Wallace E. Stegner, *Clarence Edward Dutton: An Appraisal* (Salt Lake City, Utah [1935], p. 10; George F. Becker, "Major C. E. Dutton," *American Journal of Science,* 4th ser., XXXIII (April, 1912), 387-388.

15. "Locked Book" entry for December 23, 1854, Joseph Henry Personal Papers, Smithsonian Institutuion Archives (henceforth SI Archives); Journal of Spencer

F. Baird, March 6, 1871, *ibid.;* on informality see, Simon Newcomb, *The Reminiscences of an Astronomer* (Boston, 1903), p. 243.

16. Hugh McCulloch, *Men and Measures of Half a Century* (New York, 1888), pp. 261-262.

17. "Dr. Gallaudet's Remarks," undated, box labeled "Some Papers Presented at Meetings," Literary Society of Washington Papers, Manuscript Division, Library of Congress (henceforth LC); something of the character of meetings is evoked in George C. Schaeffer to Alexander D. Bache, Saturday, 1861, RH 2243, and Joseph Henry to Bache, December 11, 1861, Box 29, Henry to Bache, February 17, 1870, RH 3492, Box 41, William J. Rhees Collection, Henry E. Huntington Library and Art Gallery.

18. McCulloch, *Men and Measures,* p. 259; Joseph Henry to Horatio King, December 20, 1870, King Papers, V, LC.

19. See, *Proceedings of the Washington Scientific Association* (Philadelphia, 1862).

20. Diary of Mary Henry, January 20, 1866, II, SI Archives; Journal of Joseph Henry, January 14, 1871, *ibid.;* Thomas Coulson, *Joseph Henry, His Life and Work* (Princeton, 1950), p. 282.

21. Joseph Henry, "Anniversary Address of the President of the Philosophical Society of Washington," November 18, 1871, *Bulletin of the Philosophical Society of Washington,* I (March, 1871-June, 1874), viii; the initiatory letter to Henry, February 7, 1871, is in the undated box labeled "Material of Historical Interest," Philosophical Society of Washington Archives, United States Naval Research Laboratory (henforth PSW Archives) and published in *ibid.,* 19-20 (subsequent to my research the PSW Archives were transferred to the SI Achives); Journal of Joseph Henry, March 6, 1871, SI Archives.

22. Henry, *Bulletin,* I (1871-1874), v.

23. *Ibid.,* viii.

24. Joseph Henry, "Annual Address of the President," November 24, 1877, *ibid.,* II (1874-1878), 162.

25. Minutes of the General Committee, March 2, 1889, PSW Archives.

26. Henry, *Bulletin,* II (1874-1878), 162; Asaph Hall, "Annual Address of the President," December 5, 1885, *ibid.,* VIII (1885), xlvi.

27. Francois N. Frenkiel, "Origin and Early Days of the Philosophical Society of Washington," *ibid.*, XVI (1962), 19; William H. Dall, *ibid.*, XII (1892-1894), 562; W. J. Humphreys, *The Philosophical Society of Washington Through a Thousand Meetings* (Washington, D. C., 1930), p. 8.

28. John S. Billings, *Bulletin,* XII (1892-1894), 549.

29. Charles V. Riley, *ibid.,* XII (1892-1894), 557; William Healey Dall, *Spencer Fullerton Baird: A Biography* (Philadelphia, 1915), pp. 231-232; William H. Holmes, *Twenty-Fifth Anniversary,* p. 45.

30. Marcus Baker to Spencer F. Baird, December 28, 1887, Letters Received from Washington Societies, SI Archives.

31. Henry, *Bulletin,* I (1871-1874), x.

32. Billings, *ibid.,* XII (1892-1894), 550.

33. Charles Petrie, *The Carlton Club* (London, 1955), p. 41.

34. Asaph Hall, *Bulletin,* (1885), xlvi; Herbert Spencer to Samuel P. Langley, February 28, 1885, Langley Papers, University of Michigan Library; Allan Nevins, *Henry White: Thirty Years of American Diplomacy* (New York, 1930), p. 104; "We have not allowed any learned association coming here for a meeting, or any man of eminence in the learned world to visit the city, without, if the case was known to our members, tendering our hospitalities. We thus aim to show the world at large what Washington is trying to be and to do." Simon Newcomb, *Twenty-Fifth Anniversary,* p. 34.

35. Humphrey Ward, *History of the Athenaeum, 1824-1925* (London, 1926), p. 14; John Timbs, *Club Life of London . . .* (London, 1866), I, 241-242.

36. Joseph Henry to S. Mann, April 6, 1876, Henry Papers, XLVIII, SI Archives.

37. Henry, *Bulletin,* I (1871-1874), xiv; Journal of Joseph Henry, November 17, 1871, SI Archives.

38. Diary of Mary Henry, January 3, 1865, II, SI Archives.

39. Albert Williams, Jr. to George F. Becker, May 4, 1883, Becker Papers, Box 15, LC.

40. Samuel F. Emmons to George F. Becker, May 30, 1883, *ibid.*

41. Newcomb, *North American Review,* CXIX (October, 1874), 286-308, and, CXXII (January, 1876), 88-123. Doubtless Newcomb's negative interpretation of natural science "was a contrived one, attempting to demonstrate the poor state of national science in the past decades." Lurie, "Science in the Nineteenth Century," *Journal of World History,* VIII (1965), 685fn.

42. Henry to My Dear [Alexander Dallas] Bache, August 9, 1838, *Science in Nineteenth-Century America: A Documentary History,* ed. Nathan Reingold (New York, 1964), p. 83.

43. Agassiz to My dear Young Chief [Alexander Dallas Bache], March 6, 1863, *ibid.,* p. 203; Edward Lurie, *Louis Agassiz: A Life in Science* (Chicago, 1960), p. 324.

44. Billings, *Bulletin,* IX (1886), xxxvii.

45. Joseph Henry, "Annual Address of the President," November 24, 1877, *ibid.,* II (1874-1878), 162; the importance of the distinction between "advancement" and "diffusion" is explained in Daniels, "Process of Professionalization," *Isis,* LVIII (Summer, 1967); 159-160.

46. "Organization of the Mathematical Section, 1883," PSW Archives.

47. Hall, *Bulletin,* VIII (1885), xlvi.

48. Billings, *ibid.,* IX (1886), xxxvii.

49. G. K. Gilbert, "Statistics of the Philosophical Society from its Formation," *ibid,* X (1888), 35.

50. Muriel Rukeyser, *Willard Gibbs* (Garden City, N.Y., 1942; Dutton paperback edn., New York, 1964), p. 316.

51. G. Brown Goode, "Four Hundredth Meeting," *Bulletin,* XII (1892-1894), 549.

52. Joel Barlow to Thomas Jefferson, September 15, 1800, Jefferson Papers, CVII, microfilm reel 36, LC.

53. James D. Dana to Othniel C. Marsh [February, 1867], Marsh Letterbooks, Peabody Museum, Yale University.

54. P. A. Siljestrom, *The Educational Institutions of the United States, Their Character and Organization,* trans. Frederica Rowan (London, 1853), p. 386.

55. Henry, *Bulletin,* II (1874-1878), 162.

56. Dall, *ibid,* XII (1892-1894), 562.

57. Samuel P. Langley to Marcus Baker, November 5, 1888, PSW Archives.

58. Minutes of the General Committee, November 26, 1898, *ibid.*

4

By A Social Tie

The imperative of organizatonal congruity dictated a close relationship between the Philosophical Society and the Cosmos Club. Thirty-six of the Club's sixty founders came from the Society, and its first officers were all Society members. Indirectly the Society could claim partial credit for the Club's existence, and from the very beginning it provided the core of the Club's membership. Once the strength of this formative influence is taken into account it becomes understandable why the manifesto of Washington's Cosmos Club has a familiar ring: "the advancement of its members in science, literature, [and] their mutual improvement by social intercourse."[1]

Here was yet another organization dedicated to individual cultivation and the enhancement of local culture. However, from its earliest moments, the Cosmos Club could not be confused with the city's elegant circles. Instead of being an association in which almost any interested party might be considered eligible for membership, the Cosmos was a highly selective body limited to those who were actually contributing to knowledge. As the representative of a Washington economics association acknowledged to Lester Frank Ward, one of the founders, "the 'Cosmos Club' is really a Club, & unlike our Assn. which some call a Club."[2] It was, therefore, *sui generis;* and because of its uniqueness the Cosmos immediately became the headquarters of Washington's intellectual elite.

Clubs were not unknown in the Capital City, nor did the Cosmos represent the first attempt to establish a club primarily for men of science. Joseph Henry's circle took the appellation "Scientific Club" as early as 1854 and went by that name for nearly twenty years. In 1871, however, its transformation into the Philosophical Society terminated its club status, leaving only the Potomac-Side Naturalists Club to meet the needs of local scientists. Created in 1858 for the purpose of drawing together students of fauna and flora in the immediate vicinity, the Naturalists Club was just slightly less venerable than the Scientific Club and had an almost equally impressive roster of members. By the mid-1870's it had grown steadily; had established a special botanical section; had found a permanent meeting place, and acquired patrons who made possible the publication of a monthly which in three years time expanded from twelve to twenty-two pages. Its journal, *Field and Forest,* was designed not only as a medium for inspiring a popular appreciation for natural history, but also to insure that "the Club shall no longer hide its light under a bushel." By its own estimation the Naturalists had come a long way. Moreover, Club spokesmen were confident that its usefulness was bound to increase, and they invoked a fitting metaphor to illustrate that in science "some of the most sturdy oaks have sprung from acorns like this one."[3]

In certain respects the Potomac-Side Naturalists showed weaknesses which cast doubt upon its ability to stand as an enduring institution. For instance, the curtailment of meetings during the Civil War was a subtle indication that it lacked the viability of Henry's aggregation, which continued in full swing throughout the conflict. More serious was its refusal to develop a permanent structure. As late as 1875 the Club's founders still were praised for adopting the "simplest plan of operation," and it was a matter of considerable pride that the Potomac-Side Naturalists carried on "without machinery to get out of order—without even an officer excepting the the Secretary . . . ."[4]

This brand of anti-institutionalism was pre-war, dating back to the time when all along a broad front, more or less authoritarian structures were assailed as inhibitors of individual expression. "The War as idea and experience" had the effect of blunting this impulse, and in its aftermath many intellectuals tended to accept and participate in the institutionalization of national culture. Organization building became the order of the day, and the imaginative men who refashioned the Scientific Club were not the only ones to be persuaded of its efficacy.[5] Yet even in the face of this development the Naturalists remained implacable. Before long the "Potomac-Side" portion of their title took on a meaning that was ironically appropriate, for clearly they were not in the institutional mainstream, and as they continued to abjure the flow of postwar culture their group became something of an anachronism. To its most loyal members the Club lost none of its appeal, but it simply was not equal to the task of assuming a major role in the creation of Washington's intellectual establishment.

Another predecessor of the Cosmos was the Metropolitan Club which drew many members from scientific and educational institutions. Joseph Henry, Theodore Nicholas Gill, and Spencer Baird represented the Smithsonian; James C. Welling academia; Benjamin Peirce, Julius Hilgard, Richard Cutts and Carlisle Patterson the Coast and Geodetic Survey; Albert J. Myer and Adolphus W. Greely the Army Signal Service; Joseph K. Barnes the Surgeon General's office; John G. Parke and Andrew A. Humphreys the Corps of Army Engineers; Charles H. Davis the Naval Observatory; Charles S. Boggs the Lighthouse Board; James Alden the Bureau of Navigation; and J. H. C. Coffin the *Nautical Almanac*. Many, of course, were in the National Academy and the Philosophical Society, and gave the Metropolitan a modicum of intellectual distinctiveness. But as with the Potomac-Side Naturalists, inherent weaknesses prevented this club from contributing much to the development of an intellectual community. Originally established in October 1863, the Metropolitan dissolved after only four years, started up again in 1872, and underwent a third reorganization in 1882. Its sporadic history seems to have offered the Cosmos Club founders a model of what to avoid. In contrast to the Naturalists the Metropolitan did have a written constitution and by-laws, the usual elected officers, and an executive committee to carry on its business. These practices would be adopted by the Cosmos Club. Moreover, like the Cosmos, it sought to provide a social outlet for men new to the capital who had accepted positions in expanding bureaus and departments. "To promote social and literary intercourse and enjoyment among its members" was the purpose set forth in its first constitution.[6]

The Metropolitan Club was so steeped in sociability that it never enjoyed the kind of group spirit which became such an important feature of the Cosmos Club. At the time of its rebirth in 1873, when enthusiasm should have been high, the annual meeting drew only ten members. Creating and maintaining interest in the Club posed a perpetual problem. During the mid-seventies foreign diplomats stationed in Washington automatically received membership invitations, but there was only one acceptance, that by the Turkish Minister Aristarchi Bey.[7]

This absence of *esprit de corps* stemmed from the fact that the Metropolitan really was not very private, as illustrated by the openness of Club functions. Attendance at its soirees was a matter of social repute. Its dinners, lectures, and art exhibits tended to be broadly based rather than exclusive. Moreover, there was no common bond of professional identity among the members. Joseph Henry, secretary of the Smithsonian Institution, and New York Congressman James Brooks, who was later censured for his implication in the Credit Mobilier scandal, shared few interests. Virtually everyone associated with official Washington was gathered into the Metropolitan—from Abraham Lincoln to Nellie Grant's glamorous husband, Algernon Sartoris. Not only was the Club membership large (the limit was set at 500), but it was also expensive. When Senator James McMillan of Michigan joined, in 1889, the cost was $150— six times the fee charged by the Cosmos Club.[8]

Another difference between the Cosmos Club and the Metropolitan was the latter's lack of discrimination in selecting members. The ease with which one might join the Metropolitan was revealed in an anecdote told by Clifford Richardson, who had come to Washington in 1878 as a scientific staff assistant in the Department of Agriculture.

> As I was passing the Club on the 8th day of July 1881 Captain George Dewey, who was sitting at an open window on H Street, hailed me and said, "Come in and have a cocktail!" I accepted the offer. In the course of conversation my host said, "Why don't you join the Club?" I replied that I had thought myself too young to do so. However, my name was put up. . . .

> The next day I met Colonel Archibald Hopkins, the Secretary of the Club, in the street. He stopped me and spoke of my nomination, adding that the Board of Governors would not meet until the following November but said that I might as well consider myself as elected and use the Club immediately. I did so without hesitation.[9]

The Cosmos Club was far less loosely composed.

The beginnings of the Cosmos Club can be traced to the fall of 1878 when a small group of government scientists, unhappy with previous attempts to create the proper social atmosphere for intellectual activity, decided to establish a club in Washington for their own use. At the initiation of Major C. E. Dutton, Garrick Mallery, and John Wesley Powell, preliminary soundings were taken among geologists to ascertain the feelings of likely founders. The results were heartening and, after a more exhaustive canvass of the U. S. Naval Observatory and the Smithsonian, it was decided to forge ahead with the project. On November 16 an informal group assembled at Powell's house where it was resolved to organize a social club composed of "men devoted to or interested in science, professionally or otherwise."[10] Temporary officers were named and a subsequent meeting called for Monday the 25th of November, at which time a constitution was adopted marking the Club's official inception. When Spencer Baird returned home that night, before turning in he noted that the weather had been exceptionally fair and mild, something which augured well for the future of the Club.[11]

Considerable latitude was rendered to qualifications for admission, and though at the outset it was referred to as the "Scientific Club of Washington,"[12] there were, among the founders, some men who were not scientists. Marcellus Bailey was a patent attorney, and Henry Adams an author; John Jay Knox a banker, and Charles Valentine Riley an agriculturalist; Edward M. Gallaudet, James C. Welling, and Daniel Coit Gilman presided over centers of higher education. Gilman, recently installed at The Johns Hopkins University, pointed out how the social union of his faculty gave rise to an intellectually stimulating environment.[13]

Among the original members were also surgeons and physicians, including: Joseph M. Toner, Newton L. Bates, Robert Fletcher, George Peck, and John Shaw Billings. Although Theodore Frelinghuysen Dwight was a librarian, several founders were career officers in the army and navy, usually scientists in uniform. One of the notable features of the Cosmos Club was its disposition to transcend professional boundaries in choosing members. "Nearly all the well-known artists, architects, and men of letters at the capital belong to it," reported *Harper's Weekly,* "and every stranger who has made his mark in one of the liberal professions finds its doors wide open to him when he visits the city."[14] However, membership was not meant to be honorific; rather it was instrumental. Association with the Club acted subtly to advance in their chosen specialties men of unmistakable promise, individuals who were rapidly moving ahead.

The fathers of The Cosmos Club did not define excellence narrowly. On the contrary, their plan revealed an admirable harmony of discrimination and diversity. Restrictive in the sense that members were carefully selected, the criteria for selection permitted a wide range of interests. Dr. Langley affirmed this on the occasion of the Club's silver anniversary:

> One of the best preparations for a proper mind in which to meet . . . changes of scientific doctrine lies, then, in the catholic spirit in which we may look out on all life, not on the scientific life alone, and this spirit is fostered in a club which opens its doors wide to all thought, and whose motto might be "nothing human is foreign to me."[15]

The intellectual range of the founders and the Club's general character were no less broad than knowledge itself, and, like the cosmos from which its name was taken, the Club represented an orderly whole in which there was a place for everything.

Seemingly the founders drew inspiration from Henry Adams by seeking that "unity through multiplicity" which so fascinated him.[16] His personal and scholarly quests for the rationalization and ordering of mind and culture were realized by the creators of the Cosmos Club. The Club contained multitudes, yet all were fused into a coherent whole by the synthesizing factor of professional worthiness. In 1882 the Washington *Evening Star* complained that whereas clubs for the "average American citizen" were becoming plentiful throughout the land, there was scant evidence that the trend had reached the capital.[17] Apparently the Cosmos Club, which had been in operation for four years, did not fall into this category—and properly so, for the Cosmos was more attuned to merit than the democratic mean. An early report stated frankly and proudly that "no club recruited from our own class of men had previously existed in the city," and, as its members have always enjoyed pointing out: there are many clubs in the cosmos, but only one Cosmos.[18]

This singularity was heightened by the Club's aim to "make a place where it will be possible for the members of the Club to meet socially at any time under pleasant surroundings."[19] Intimacy and charm were to be its hallmarks, and the "mutual improvement" of the membership was to be gained through "social intercourse." Thus, it was not extraordinary for outsiders to describe it as a "company of distinguished workers in various fields of public usefulness who gather for social relaxation within the hospitable walls of the Cosmos . . . ." Unlike The Literary, the Philosophical, and the new professional societies, members did not join together for the purpose of reading weighty disquisitions to one another. Casualness was the very essence of its style. Aside from the annual elections each January, and monthly business meetings, there were no functions in which members were obliged to take part.

> Its members do not assemble to . . . air their scholarly attainments, but for recreation purely; and the use they make of their time when off duty is well attested to by the merry click of the billiard balls, the gathering around the chess tables, the animated chatter of the smoking-rooms, and the drafts made nightly upon the mass of popular magazines and weeklies with which the tables are strewn.[20]

This tone of gracious informality yields an insight into why its founders considered a new and different type of organization so necessary.

The social ambiance of the Cosmos Club was intended to kindle a spirit of community among Washington's intellectuals, especially those involved in government sponsored and orientated science. By filling the void left by the Philosophical Society it was felt that the Club would alleviate the kind of fear and suspicion which tended to crop up among those engaged in research, and, conversely, create a mood of mutual appreciation and good will. Grove Karl Gilbert, one of the disgruntled geologists in the Society, put it succinctly when he said that the Cosmos Club endeavored to "bind the scientific men of Washington by a social tie and thue promote that solidarity which is important to their proper work and influence."[21]

Of more than passing interest is the fact that a similar type of infrastructure would soon be created by the Republican leadership of the United States Senate. Sometime around 1890, as the Upper House assumed its modern forms of party machinery, chamber rules, regularized procedures, chairman superintendency, committee operations, and roll call discipline, what was dubbed the School of Philosophy Club emerged on Vermont Avenue, only a short distance—both figuratively and literally—from the Cosmos Club. This innovation was designed to accommodate the new, organization-minded professional who was gaining influence through cohesiveness. Its motif was social, and rarely were political words exchanged over the billiard table, among the poker players, or between the occupants of its comfortable leather chairs. Yet the School of Philosophy Club was, in a sense, the political counterpart of the Cosmos Club, for "a strong personal comradeship united the men gathering there. At times the friendships induced a participant to vote against his better judgment but most often the fellowship simply insured that good feeling prevailed among the gentlemen who dominated the Senate. No doubt it served them well as they settled public questions and adjusted private ambitions."[22]

The "social tie" of the Cosmos Club served to improve communications among the scientific corps while facilitating vital contacts between scientists and politicians. Association with the Club soon became an effective way to keep abrest of professional news. "I haven't given you much gossip," apologized Samuel F. Emmons to a fellow geologist, whereupon he referred his correspondent to another man who was bound to be a better source of enlightenment, "for he goes regularly to the Cosmos, and plays cards with the Major [Powell] , Gilbert & Co."[23] When Gilbert sought some particulars concerning meteorology in the Federal Government he turned to the Club, and "asked various questions of various people" as the surest route to reliable information.[24]

Equally important was the way the Club functioned as a sheltered meeting ground for Washington's intellectual leaders, an inconspicuous base of operations, and a kind of informal conduit to the centers of political power. For example, it was in the Cosmos Club, during the National Academy of Sciences meeting in April, 1889, that Thomas C. Mendenhall quietly received word that he was the establishment's candidate to head the Coast and Geodetic Survey. "We are going to have you back here bye & bye as Supt. of the Coast Survey," was how he recalled Powell's remark. President Benjamin Harrison's desk was already piled high with applications, but there were ways of circumventing that detail to insure Mendenhall's appointment. Cosmos Club member Gardiner Greene Hubbard arranged a dinner so that "a few of the leading government officials" could meet "a few members of the Academy." Mendenhall was carefully seated next to Treasury Secretary William Windom whose department had overall responsibility for the Coast Survey. Gaining Windom's ear led to his backing, and the Secretary emerged as Mendenhall's advocate in the decision making circle of the Administration. In July the two went together to the White House where Harrison had Mendenhall's commission awaiting the necessary signatures. By then it had dawned on Mendenhall that "the arrangement by which I was seated next to Mr. Windom, the Sec'y of the Treasury, was made with 'malice aforethought' although I suspected nothing of the kind at the time."[25] Certainly his surprise was not shared by Powell.

Powell's larger objectives in such matters were artfully conceived and resourcefully planned for, as evidenced by an 1884 letter marked "personal." "As you know," he wrote candidly to his colleague George F. Becker, "I am trying to build up the Geological Survey to a position, as one of the bureaus of the Government, in which it can do efficient service. . . . In order to grow from year to year, it is necessary to interest a larger body of legislators and to obtain the friendly cooperation of the public press."[26] The means he employed for achieving these ends are illuminated by an entry in the diary of Edward M. Gallaudet, referring to a dinner engagement with his Cosmos Club compatriot: "At 6:30 P.M. I started out to take dinner with Major J. W. Powell. I found at his table Robert Lincoln, Secretary of War, Gov. Kirkwood, the Secretary of the Interior, Senators Davis, Logan, & Cameron. . . ."[27] In such ways would the Cosmos Club contribute to a leavening of American science and culture.

Under Powell's guidance the Club became an immediate success. As early as 1880 it had expanded its facilities and begun holding weekly "Club Nights" which occasioned particularly good turn outs. Some members, like Clarence King, still found Washington uncongenial, "a place of such transient residence that permanent friendships, which are, after all, the mitigating circumstances of life, seem out of the question."[28] But King was virtually in a class by himself. As his friend John Hay said, "There ought to be more like him but I suppose the Almighty could not afford it, at the price."[29]

During the summer of 1883 the Smithsonian's Tarleton Bean and G. Brown Goode journeyed to England for the International Fisheries Exhibition, and, quipped Baird, "to study the fishes of the British Museum." One of the most striking features of London's intellectual atmosphere was the intense jealousy among scientists—"quite in contrast with the ordinary condition of things at home," they reported.[30] Bean and Goode were active in the Cosmos Club, and, as insiders, they could apprehend its full significance for Washington's men of mind.

One of the foremost achievements of the Cosmos Club were making the intellectual community more coherent, tightening the natural bonds that would enable government scientists and scholars to function with greater effectiveness. This required forceful direction which, in the beginning, was resisted by the Philosophical Society. Indeed there existed within the Society a feeling that the Cosmos Club could threaten its very existence. As a social organization whose members were chosen with even greater care, the Cosmos did not exactly duplicate the older group. On the other hand, there were enough similarities between the two to suggest that the Club's development might progress at the expense of the Society. Some feared that a flourishing Club would emasculate the Society by absorbing its important members, and they construed the founding of the Cosmos Club as overweening ambition for organizational supremacy.

Against this backdrop a sequence of events unfolded which had all the fast-moving excitement of a carefully staged melodrama. The action opened less than a month after the historic meeting at Powell's house when it became known that the Philosophical Society would shortly be recast along club lines, thereby guaranteeing its self-preservation and mounting a challenge to the Cosmos Club's reason for being. This decision was to be carried out on December 12, 1878, at a meeting scheduled for eight o'clock at the Army Medical Museum. Quickly Powell and a few others moved to foil the Society's plan. They decided to hold an emergency meeting of the Cosmos Club on the same date, at the same place, but to have it begin promptly at 7:30 P.M., half an hour before the Society was set to convene. The single item of business was a resolution enabling anyone in the Philosophical Society to join the Club before January 1, 1879. This was rushed through without delay, allowing plenty of time for Welling, who was in both groups, to step across the hall and present a general invitation to the

Society's assembled membership. By this gambit the movement to transform the Philosophical Society into a club collapsed, with the Cosmos making several immediate additions to its number.[31]

Where previously had stood a single bona fide intellectual organization, there now were two, and the interlocking leadership of the Cosmos Club and the Philosophical Society made the Washington community a more potent element in national culture. By 1879 the intellectuals had provided themselves with a firmer structural base from which to exert—if not power—at least the next best thing to power, influence.

Influence poses an elusive problem for historical study because it seldom lends itself to conventional documentation. As a species of covert behavior it is, by definition, subtle and surreptitious. Influence has to do with quite conversation, discreet persuasion, cajolery, and forms of delicate pressure that may never receive literal description. It means establishing confidences, cultivating friendships, and forming associations too intimate to be recorded. Since the very essence of influence is not leaving traces, it is inaccessible to orthodox methodology. Hence, the historian must rely on evidence that is circumstantial, inferential, or presumptive.[32] This becomes critical when measuring the general significance of Washington's intellectual community, particularly so when assessing the dominant role of the Cosmos Club in strengthening the late nineteenth-century nexus of science and politics.

A case in point concerns the Club's part in the reordering of western geographical and geological work. Between 1867 and 1874 four separate surveys were commissioned to study rock strata in the far west and to investigate whether any use could be made of this last, unsettled part of the country. Dr. Ferdinand V. Hayden's United States Geological Survey of the Territories was first into the field, followed shortly by the United States Geological Exploration of the Fortieth Parallel, led by Clarence King, the United States Geological Survey West of the One Hundredth Meridian, with Lieutenant George Montague Wheeler in charge, and Powell's United States Geographical and Geological Survey of the Rocky Mountain Region. From what Indians called the summit of the world, near Yellowstone, to the alkali flats of Nevada's Great Basin, and from the drifting sands of Death Valley to the turbulent waters of the lower Colorado the explorations and surveys traversed America's most majestic sections, leaving behind them a long list of noteworthy achievements. They provided reliable maps of what had hitherto been *terra incognita*. They opened the way for miners, ranchers, lumbermen, and railroad builders. Through their descriptive writings, photographs, paintings, and sketches they popularized an image of the west which was at once credible and enthralling. As a result of their collections of Indian artifacts, myths, and vocabularies they gave momentum to the study of American ethnology. In geology, botany, and paleontology, their efforts were so fruitful that they influenced permanently the earth sciences. Withstanding formidable hardships and dangers the expeditions carried out their tasks with enthusiasm and competence, completing many technical projects and setting guidelines for even more. "Eighteen hundred and sixty-seven," wrote Clarence King, "marks, in the history of national geological work, a turning point, when the science ceased to be dragged in the dust of rapid exploration and took a commanding position in the professional work of the country."[33] It is with good reason that they have come to be called "the Great Surveys."[34]

By the late 1870's, however, their greatness was threatening to put them out of business. Less and less of the west was unknown, and now that good railroad track beds had been found and rich silver deposits identified, the overlapping and duplication of the surveys became nettlesome to Congress. It was Congress which held the power of life and death over the surveys since they were provided for not by statutes, but through annual appropriations. In 1874, after broaching the subject of combining the various surveys, the House Committee on Public Lands had concluded that such action could be postponed. But four years later the Appropriations Committee of the House announced that further funds would be withheld until organizational inefficiencies were overcome. There could now be no doubt that the time for decision had arrived. Unless the surveys were consolidated scientific investigation in the west would cease altogether. Expressions of concern had already been heard from the ranks of science, most notably Josiah Dwight Whitney's extended article in the *North American Review* calling attention to the fact that several surveys were performing virtually the same functions in more or less the same territories, and Congress could not be expected to abide this condition indefinitely.[35]

The congressional warning of 1878 found a significant body of scientists favorably disposed toward the reorganization of western research. When the National Academy of Sciences was instructed to report on how geological and geographical surveys could be streamlined, a select committee composed of Alexander Agassiz, James Dwight Dana, acting President O. C. Marsh, J. S. Newberry, Simon Newcomb, William Barton Rogers, and William P. Trowbridge took up the problem without delay. Requests for information were sent to those in charge of existing surveys so that their ideas could be considered in preparing the final report. As it turned out, Powell's reply was used verbatim, which meant that though he had not yet been named to the National Academy he was formulating its official policy on the subject of consolidation. At its special New York meeting, November 6, 1878, the committee's (or Powell's) recommendations were adopted with only one dissenting vote. Mensuration work should be combined under the Coast and Geodetic Survey, with all investigations of natural resources in the public domain and classification of public lands becoming the responsibility of a new bureau in the Interior Department, the United States Geological Survey.[36] If acted upon by Congress this would eliminate the Great Surveys.

Ultimately this consolidation was achieved, but not without a struggle and only after the National Academy's original plan had been watered down. History has remembered the acrimonious debates of the Forty-Fifth Congress. The sessions were punctuated with controversies over the size, support, and internal uses of the army; the remonetization of silver and its relationship to gold; resumption of specie payments; alleged frauds and voting irregularities in the presidential election of 1876; and the restriction of Chinese immigration. The recasting of government geological and geographical work did nothing to ease this *Sturm und Drang*. When advocates of the National Academy's proposals declared that consolidation would represent a substantial savings of money, opponents retorted that this was false economy, since discontinuing Lieutenant Wheeler's Survey would deprive the army of a vital intelligence source for waging Indian campaigns, "and unless this information is obtained by the War Department disastrous results are liable to follow at any time."[37] The point about reducing bureaucratic waste was challenged by those who maintained that the Coast Survey, which was to have jurisdiction over surveys of mensuration, was overstaffed, uneconomical, and "the most irresponsible and extravagant scientific body that Congress has ever provided for." Denying that unification was truly progressive, the anti-consolidation forces argued that such a change in the system of parcelling out unsettled territory would raise "unnumbered hinderances to the prompt obtaining of title to homes by the hardy pioneers of our country."[38] Conservationist claims were dismissed brusquely: "Pay these scientific men to hunt bugs, pay them to get up fancy colored maps, and yet charge the settler with the expense of defining the boundaries of his little homestead!"[39] Clearly the opposition was too strong for the National Academy's plan to be passed intact. However, the section calling for a new geological survey under the Interior Department did carry, as a rider to the Sundry Civil Appropriation Act, which was signed by President Hayes on March 3, 1879.

Before the ink was dry there were murmurs of complaint about the role played in these proceedings by a coterie of local intellectuals led by Powell. "The scheme had had its origin here in Washington," groused Montana Congressman Martin Maginnis, "in the lobbies of the House—scientific lobbyists perhaps—certainly scientific in the manner in which they have conducted their approaches on this body." Maginnis, who disdained "the conceit of new-fledged collegiates and of governmental scientists," had little use for the Capital City's savants. Yet, in a backhanded fashion, he was crediting them with proficiently managing their cause and, by way of innuendo, the highest tribute went to Powell.[40]

Powell's singular contribution came in the form of two government reports printed in 1878, *Lands of the Arid Region of the United States,* and *Methods of Surveying the Public Domain.*[41] These *tours de force* not only demonstrated the value of his own survey, they also presented a convincing argument in favor of revising federal land policies so that Washington could plan for both the development and the conservation of western territories. *Lands of the Arid Region,* published over the signature of Secretary of the Interior Schurz, was distributed by the all-important House Committee on Appropriations, and, of course, *Methods of Surveying the Public Domain* was actually the National Academy's report recommending unification. These documents enabled influential friends of science in both parties—especially Democrats John D. C. Atkins, Chairman of Appropriations in the House, his fellow committee member Abram S. Hewitt, and Congressman James A. Garfield, leader of the Republican minority—to build a persuasive case for the creation of a United States Geological Survey. Also, Clarence King, Powell's candidate for the directorship of the Survey, was put in charge of the new enterprise, while at the same time Congress went along with two of the Major's favorite designs for promoting science: requiring that all collections made by federal surveys be deposited in the National Museum, and instituting a Bureau of Ethnology as part of the Smithsonian. By the end of the congressional session Powell had carried all before him. "There can be no doubt that this whole thing came about with various other changes of a revolutionary character, through the instrumentality of the Major," wrote ethnologist Frank Hamilton Cushing.[42]

Where did the Cosmos Club fit into this chain of successes? "Some perturbed individuals" saw its formation as the central link in a "scheme to control governmental scientific activities."[43] Presumably these "perturbed individuals" were Powell's enemies, men who resented his accomplishments, envied his political instincts, and who divined in his every action a larger campaign of aggrandizement which would end with the Major and a detachment of chosen lieutenants in command of American science. Having captured government geology he was now preparing to move on other fronts. Accordingly, the easy inference followed that Powell founded the Cosmos Club to further his own purposes in the scientific establishment.

A better understanding of Powell's relationship to the Club can be gained by turning this conventional interpretation on its head, and considering the question from the standpoint of Powell needing the Club less than it needed him. At the same time, the extent of his ambitions and the nature of his motives must be placed in proper perspective. Outright control was beyond his grasp. More realistically he sought influence, generating action by convincing or manipulating men of power rather than power itself.[44] His ultimate goal, maximizing the potential of national science, called for viable institutions whose authority would be more solidly entrenched than that of individuals. Taking this into consideration changes the Cosmos Club from a subordinate to a primary objective. Powell's critics began with a valid assumption: the consolidation of the Surveys and the establishment of the Cosmos were not merely coincidental, and his achievements were inseparable from the Club's successful beginning. Their fallacy lay in inverting the emphasis, for Powell contributed far more to the Club than he could possibly have gained from it.

In 1879 the national image and reputation of the Cosmos Club was derived from its most illustrious members, John Wesley Powell and Clarence King. Powell had already garnered the esteem of leading men of science through his report for the National Academy, and, like King, he enjoyed a widespread popular following. Through their exploits both had gained such notoriety that mere mention of the names Powell and King immediately conjured up images familiar to the public. Powell, the one-armed explorer, captured the public's fancy in 1869 when he and his party were believed to have disappeared in a whirlpool while attempting to navigate the tempestuous Green River. Soon afterward "The King of Diamonds" created a sensation by exposing a cache of fradulant gems that had convinced none other than Charles Tiffany. Men who narrowly escaped being bilked thanked God and Clarence King in the same breath, thereby showing how close the latter had come to immortality.[45] On the professional level, the reputations of King and Powell were enhanced by the publication of such monographs as *Mountaineering in the Sierra*

Nevada and Powell's *Exploration of the Colorado River.* These two had also been assiduously courting official Washington for years before the Club was convinced.[46] Thus, while the history of consolidation would likely have been the same without the Cosmos Club, it is impossible to imagine how the Club could have begun as it did without King and Powell.

Powell simply did not need the Club to gain acceptance for consolidation. His plan for reorganizing federally sponsored geology offered several patent advantages. On the level of expediency it provided a timely alternative to the surveys of Wheeler and Hayden, both of which suffered from critical limitations, being continued only by the grace of bureaucratic inertia. For all practical purposes the kind of topographical reconnaissance undertaken by Wheeler had perished in the Civil War, along with other projects of soldier-scientists that earlier had contributed mightily to the winning of the west.[47] Indeed, one of the few excuses for resurrecting the military survey in 1871 was that map-making had always been a legitimate army function. During its history the United States Geographical Survey West of the One Hundredth Meridian made some contributions to paleontology, botany, ornithology, and zoology, thanks to civilian employees like Fielding Bradford Meek, as well as Cosmos Club founders G. K. Gilbert, Henry W. Henshaw, and Henry C. Yarrow. Yet, the inherent rigidity of the army way proved inhibiting and, by 1878, all save the Corps of Engineers agreed that abolishing Wheeler's Survey would be a good thing.[48]

A significant body of opinion also favored disbanding the survey headed by Ferdinand V. Hayden, but for different reasons. Unlike Wheeler's, the Hayden enterprise was primarily geological and as such it was more relevant to the needs of national science. Being part of the Interior Department it enjoyed a civilian status rendering it estimable in the eyes of the scientific establishment. Its professional staff—including Cyrus Thomas, William Henry Holmes, Henry Gannett, Frederick Endlich, Edward Drinker Cope, one of the leading vertebrate paleontologists in the country, and "the Nestor of American paleobotanists—Leo Lesquereux" was superior to Wheeler's. Beginning in 1867 and for the next eleven years it uncovered great portions of natural history. The photographs of William Henry Jackson and the landscape paintings of Thomas Moran kept it consistently in the public eye. It was valued by western agriculturalists, railroad promoters, and miners; and the entrepreneurial skill of its director made it increasingly popular with Congress. Indeed, the mercurial Hayden "became the most powerful and most celebrated public scientist of the seventies."[49] His survey had only one weakness—poor administration. And, by 1878, this had become an insuperable problem.

Though slight of frame, Ferdinand V. Hayden was blessed with unbounded energy which enabled him to scurry up and down mountains and across deserts like a man possessed. "There was a vehemence and a sort of wildness in his nature," recalled J. Peter Lesley. He was passionately devoted to the virgin west, adored what he termed its "beautiful decorations," and seemed determined to make known as much of it as was possible before death overtook him. With his ever-present specimen bag and geologist's pick, ferreting in winter and summer, whether accompanied by assistants or alone, Hayden became a familiar sight—as well as a curiosity—to the natives. The Sioux had a name for him: "Man-Who-Picks-Up-Stones-Running." This nervous intensity was reflected in the work of the survey. Spatially speaking it accomplished much, but more often than not this meant sacrificing detailed analysis. Self-descriptions of its manifold activities filled tomes, but all too frequently these accounts contained inacuracies that made Hayden look like either a charlatan or an incompetent. "He worked with a telescope instead of with a microscope. He worked so rapidly and published so quickly that shoddiness became the hallmark of his reports."[50] Since deliberate, methodical investigation was beyond his ken, it became clear that Hayden's Survey had—in a very literal sense—run its course.

In addition to the shortcomings of definition and administration plaguing both surveys, an internecine rivalry had grown up between them. Once Hayden and Wheeler sensed the imminence of extinction they confronted each other as implacable foes. So great was their enmity that malicious personal attacks became commonplace. Wheeler charged that his opponent lacked sufficient skill even to "revise the work done by his own topographers," whereupon Hayden vowed that "if he stirs a finger, or attempts to interfere with me or my survey in any way, I will utterly crush him—as I have enough congressional influence to do so, and will bring it to bear."[51] Such venemous give and take underscores a general condition of the pursuit of natural science in late nineteenth century America: unrelenting antipathies were the rule not the exception.

It was this problem which Powell sought to alleviate. Abolishing competing surveys would cast out one apple of discord. Similarly, requiring that all newly discovered artifacts, fossils, and specimens be deposited in national institutions (the United States Museum and the Bureau of Ethnology) aimed at curbing competition between individual specialists, such as Cope and Marsh. Their titanic struggles over the classification and description of extinct animals, pitting against each other two giants of paleontology, were exacerbated by repeated contests over fossil troves in the west. "They were," in Nathan Reingold's phrase, "Robber Barons trying to corner the old-bones market."[52] Reducing this speculative fever was bound to diminish hostilities and yield happier relations among the big plungers. Finally, an organization designed as a mollifying force promised to engender mutual trust and good will. In this way the Hayden-Wheeler fight dramatized the urgent need for the Cosmos Club and, by the same token, the Club's founding was bound up with the United States Geological Survey.

However, it did not follow from this that the Cosmos Club was indispensable to the creation of the Survey or the appointment of its personnel. Maintaining what would nowadays be termed a "low profile," the Club conveyed an impression of discreet non-involvement in consolidation quarrels. The decision that Hayden and Wheeler had become expendable was reached by scientists outside the Club's orbit. Powell's report was silent on the question of who should head the new bureau; consequently it could not be deemed unfriendly toward either antagonist. It was true that the report was slanted against military surveys, but this prejudice was widely held and certainly Powell's bias did not cause the downfall of Wheeler. Nor did the Club act to save Hayden, despite personal appeals to Spencer Baird in the former's hour of need.[53] The Cosmos Club could not easily be associated with the consignment of Hayden and Wheeler to premature retirement.

Moreover, the man who ultimately received the directorship, Clarence King, was named because he commanded "the respect and hearty support of the best scientific men in the country,"[54] not as a result of his affiliation with the Cosmos Club. King, rather than the Club, assumed the main burden of soliciting letters from these men backing his candidacy. "I am here in the thick of the fight," he wrote, after taking up a position in Washington from which to marshal support for his nomination.[55] President Hayes had already begun receiving notes favorable to King, including the glowing sentiments of William Dean Howells and a letter from Mrs. Howells to "Dear Cousin Lucy," proclaiming King "the most accomplished man of his age in the country."[56] Now messages equally saturated with praise engulfed the White House. During the first three months of 1879 Hayes heard from state geologists, the presidents and faculties of major scientific schools, members of the National Academy, as well as geologists formerly employed by the defunct surveys, notable Grove Karl Gilbert (Wheeler's), Clarence Edward Dutton (Powell's) and, of course, Powell himself. The only significant name missing belonged to

James Dwight Dana, King's old mentor at Yale and the venerable editor of *Silliman's Journal,* who felt constrained to limit himself to a course of benevolent neutrality.[57] Given this embarrassment of riches, the public voice of the Cosmos Club was hardly necessary to secure King's appointment.

Yet the Cosmos Club was not indifferent to politics, and in great and small ways the government had a bearing on its early development. The practice of admitting female guests to the Club rooms began with the celebration of President Garfield's inauguration, showing that the Club was susceptible to political infection.[58] This meant forsaking a tradition, for it had long been felt that relaxing the prohibitions against women would be an invitation to decadence. "We may, in the spirit of scientific investigation," avowed Billings, "secure good seats to inspect the latest patterns of skirt-dancing and high-kicking in the places where these are something of a specialty, but we don't want them at home."[59] Yet the political contagions of Washington caused a lowering of resistance. Moreover it was believed that the Club would eventually reciprocate by exerting influence in government. As Simon Newcomb stated emphatically: "The bringing into closer touch of the academic and the political sides of Washington should be one of our great objects."[60]

Another aim, and one most seriously pursued, was safeguarding the Club's exclusiveness. After the general invitation to the Philosophical Society, membership in the Cosmos Club was limited to two hundred. When vacancies occurred the secretary and treasurer notified the committee on admissions which, in turn, would receive proposals for new members. The candidates' names were then posted on a central bulletin board for fifteen days during which recommendations were invited and the qualifications carefully reviewed. The committee numbered ten, and only two negative ballots were necessary for rejection. Candidates who survived this test were finally passed upon by the Club, and those getting a two-thirds majority were accepted, while those who were voted down could not be renominated for twelve months. None of the other groups had membership policies that were comparably strict, but like the rest, the Cosmos Club's exclusiveness did not pertain to material status. "We have never aimed at social distinction," said Newcomb. "We invite no one to our midst because he is prominent in the eye of the public."[61]

It is noteworthy that the Cosmos Club was able to remain inexpensive without impeding its steady progress. A twenty dollar admission fee and annual dues set at a modest twenty dollars for residents and ten dollars for non-residents were the only membership costs. Understandably the operating budget was always small, and before the Club was two weeks old it became necessary to request immediate payment of individual charges in order to meet expenses. Later on, the officers were obliged to solicit voluntary subscriptions to finance special events. Even so, the unwritten rule of keeping assessments to a minimum was held inviolate.

Operating on a slender financial thread both dictated frugality and illustrated the Club's singular contacts. Overseas postage was saved on periodicals from Great Britain thanks to Theodore F. Dwight being Librarian at the State Department. Dwight arranged for the United States dispatch agent in London simply to drop printed matter for the Cosmos Club into the regular diplomatic pouch, and in this manner the Club received prompt delivery of its British newspapers and magazines—as well as a few back issues slipped in each week—at only the publication price.[62] This courtesy was another mark of uniqueness. Pride in economy was reflected in 1881—the year Henry Williamson Howgate, one of its founders, was charged with embezzling over $100,000 from the Signal Service Disbursement Office—when the board of management boasted that the Cosmos Club was far more reasonable than similar organizations in England and America.[63] Nonetheless, the Club was becoming securely established and plans for a grander clubhouse were underway.

For five years the Club rented cramped but temporary quarters on the third floor of the Corcoran Building, Fifteenth and Pennsylvania Avenue. Then it moved to Lafayette Square, first to 23 Madison Place and in 1886 up the street to the Dolley Madison House, its glorious location for the next sixty-six years. Lafayette Square ranked among the most famous landmarks in what was indisputably the most illustrious and dignified residential section of the city. Moreover the mid-eighties, when the Club took up its new residence, marked the zenith of what had customarily been known as the "President's Park," or more colloquially, "the lobby of the White House." The official name was bestowed in 1878, when Lafayette Square acquired its longest inhabitant, Henry Adams. During the next forty years Adams lived a block west of the Club, opposite the Executive Mansion in the double house Henry H. Richardson had designed specially for the Adamses and the John Hays. At once this Romanesque masterpiece became a celebrated salon presided over by the "Five of Hearts" (its occupants plus the irrepressible Clarence King), further enriching the neighborhood's legendary quality in its golden age. Across Sixteenth Street rose St. John's Episcopal Church, which claimed Washington's most fashionable congregation and which, after James Renwick's renovation in 1883, expressed masterfully the splendor of the Square. Of particular note were the new stained glass windows made, appropriately, by the curator of glass at Adams' beloved Chartres Cathedral.[64] The dwelling places adjacent to Adams, and flanking the Square, housed as they always had, cabinet members, congressmen, naval heroes, and distinguished private citizens. Except for a row of stately elms the remaining side, to the south was bare. This gave Club members and almost unimpaired view of the nation's political headquarters and, for that matter, allowed the president to look back at one of the United States' foremost intellectual centers.[65]

The Cosmos Club on Lafayette Square shortly became the common meeting site for Washington's professional societies. In 1886 an assembly hall was added to the south side of its new building, not only for the Club but for other societies as well. By renting to these groups the Cosmos showed that while there were fundamental differences between societies for the dissemination of learning and a social club, mutual assistance was desirable. The income from its tenants enabled the Club to expand its facilities without raising dues, and through the Club's standing invitations the societies were spared the expense of separate quarters. Furthermore, interrelating the Club with the societies had the effect of spinning more finely the organizational web of Washington's intellectual community. From the time of the Club's inception it was intended that local societies which were "purely literary, artistic, or scientific and in no way concerned with the regulation of business or commercial affairs" be permitted use of the assembly hall. The major prerequisites (besides demanding that guests use a separate entrance) was that the society in question have at least forty-five members from the Cosmos Club roster, and that no fewer than twenty of these men regularly attend its meetings.[66] This was hardly an impediment since dual membership was usual, most of the superior government scientiests deriving their social sustenance from the Cosmos Club.

If Joseph Henry's spirit hovered over the Philosophical Society, the Cosmos Club was personified by Powell, and its role as catalytic agent in molding the community of government scientists bespoke his image of the Club's importance. After Henry's death, when it became apparent that the Philosophical Society would not alter his legacy by capitulating to specialization, a number of particularized groups came into being. These organizations were at once causes and effects of the broadening influence of science in the federal government, and their nascent development paralleled the early histories of related public agencies. "The moment we examine closely our own national administration," observed a contributor to the *Popular Science Monthly,* "we find an amazing development in certain lines of scientific industry. Nearly every executive department either has scientific experts regularly connected with it, or employs such experts occasionally for the conduct of important investigations."[67] This trend received its most dramatic thrust from the Geological Survey, but there were many other bureaus and agencies abundantly staffed by scientists. Between Engraving and Printing, which periodically offered employment, and the Coast and Geodetic Survey, probably the most scientific in character, were the Ordnance Corps, Weather Service, Lighthouse Board, Department of Agriculture, Fish Commission, the Patent Office, Weights and Measures, military medical corps, and the Naval Observatory. The emerging professional societies heightened the effectiveness of these men as practitioners of their separate specialties, while at the Cosmos Club they found a social atmosphere that deepened appreciation of all disciplines. The Cosmos Club was therefore crucial to averting fragmentation within the scientific departments. Indeed, as the epitomy of synthesis, it was primarily responsible for keeping a balance between specialization and community. This function was consistent with Powell's whole career which was less distinguished for abstract thought or original research than for achieving harmony and order. His forte was rationalization, causing some colleagues to complain that he "wants to corral everybody."[68] Yet few would gainsay his flair for organization, or deny that in carrying out his expansive schemes he went from strength to strength—regardless of whether he was codifying Indian languages, consolidating systems of map coloration, unifying western surveys, or drawing together the members of scientific societies.

The "experiment" which Powell hoped would "at least get a fair trial"[69] had brought forth gratifying results. As a social body it subtly allied conglomerate specialists. Its effect in improving interpersonal relations was such that one could find "much in the atmosphere of Washington . . . to inspire and encourage useful activities."[70] This unification of the Capital City's men of mind helped increase their vitality. Of course these developments did not take place in a vacuum, but were interwoven with the larger patterns of late nineteenth century professional and institutional growth. Particularly germane to the Cosmos Club was the consolidation of the surveys. This triumph infused government scientists with a self-awareness of their own importance in official Washington and gave them a sense of group consciousness.[71] The establishment of the United States Geological Survey therefore redounded to the advantage of the Club, and from the time of their simultaneous founding, a reciprocal relationship developed between the two. The third piece of this mosaic which took shape in 1878-79 was the Anthropological Society of Washington, a different kind of "experiment," but again, one that yielded important results.

NOTES TO CHAPTER 4

1. Articles of Incorporation of the Cosmos Club of Washington City, *By-Laws, Rules and Regulations of the Cosmos Club* (Washington, D. C., 1879), p. 3.

2. Edward Young to Lester F. Ward, February 2, 1883, Ward Papers, Autographs, I, 29, Brown University Library.

3. Elliott Coues, "Salutatory," *Field and Forest*, I (June, 1875), 2; J. W. Chickering, "The Potomac-Side Naturalists' Club," *Science*, N. S., XXIII (February 16, 1906), 264-265; for a glimpse of Club activities over the years see Journal of Spencer F. Baird, February 18, 1861, Smithsonian Institution Archives (henceforth SI Archives), and Ward Papers, Biography, I, 40, Brown University Library.

4. Coues, *Field and Forest*, I, 1.

5. For this interpretation of the impact of the Civil War see, George M. Fredrickson, *The Inner Civil War: Northern Intellectuals and the Crisis of the Union* (New York, 1965), *passim*.

6. *Constitution, By-Laws and List of Members of the Metropolitan Club of Washington City, Organized October 1, 1863* (n.p., n.d.); John A. Barker, *A Brief History of the Metropolitan Club of Washington, with a Sketch of the Two Clubs of Similar Title Which Preceded It, Covering a Period of Nearly a Half-Century* (n.p., 1909).

7. Carl Charlick, *The Metropolitan Club of Washington: The Story of Its Men and of Its Place in City and Country* (Washington, D. C., 1964), pp. 43-45.

8. F.W. Poor to James McMillan, April 20, 1889, McMillan Papers, Burton Historical Collection, Detroit Public Library.

9. Quoted in Charlick, *Metropolitan*, p. 67.

10. J. W. Powell and Edward S. Holden to William Henry Holmes, November 18, 1878, Holmes, "Random Records of a Lifetime . . .," National Collection of Fine Arts Library, SI; this form invitation to participate in founding the Club is reprinted in William A. DeCaindry (comp.), "Documentary History of the

Cosmos Club," *The Twenty-Fifth Anniversary of the Founding of the Cosmos Club of Washington* (Washington, D. C., 1904), p. 66.

11. Journal of Spencer F. Baird, November 25, 1878, SI Archives; Kip Ross, "Fateful Meeting, Fateful Year, 1878," *Cosmos Club Bulletin*, XI (November, 1958) 2-12.

12. Powell and Holden to Holmes, November 18, 1878, "Random Records," National Collection of Fine Arts Library, SI.

13. Hugh Hawkins, "The Birth of a University: A History of The Johns Hopkins University from the Death of the Founder to the End of the First Year of Academic Work, 1873-1877" (unpublished Ph.D. dissertation, Department of History, The Johns Hopkins University, 1954), pp. 325-328; Gilman had also been a member of "The Club" at Yale during the late fifties and early sixties, an illustrious faculty circle which met to discuss science, politics, and religion, Hugh Hawkins, *Pioneer: A History of The Johns Hopkins University, 1874-1889* (Ithaca, N. Y., 1960), pp. 16-17; Fabian Franklin, *Life of Daniel Coit Gilman* (New York, 1910), chap. ii.

14. "The Cosmos Club of Washington, D. C.," *Harper's Weekly*, XXXII (September 29, 1888), 738.

15. Address delivered by Samuel Pierpont Langley, *The Twenty-Fifth Anniversary of the Cosmos Club*, p. 21.

16. Although Adams was elected to the first committee on admissions he was not noticeably active in the Club after its founding. Perhaps, in this matter, he obeyed his own maxim that "silence, next to good-temper, was the mark of sense." Henry Adams, *The Education of Henry Adams: An Autobiography* (Boston, 1918; Sentry edn., Cambridge, Mass., 1961), p. 501; on Adams being torn between "passive perception" and "reaction" see J. C. Levenson, "Henry Adams and the Art of Politics," *Southern Review*, N.S., IV (January, 1968), 50-58.

17. *The Evening Star* (Washington, D. C.), July 1, 1882, p. 2.

18. Thomas M. Spaulding, *The Cosmos Club on Lafayette Square* (Washington, D. C., 1949), p. 5; *Cosmos Club Bulletin*, I (March, 1948), 2.

19. Powell and Holden to Holmes, November 18, 1878, Holmes, "Random Records," National Collection of Fine Arts Library, SI.

20. *Harper's Weekly*, XXXII, 738; the Club's admirable collection of periodical literature is described in J. S. Patterson to Lester F. Ward, March 25, 1885, Ward Papers, Autographs, I, 50, Brown University Library.

21. Address delivered by Grove Karl Gilbert, *The Twenty-Fifth Anniversary of the Cosmos Club*, p. 40.

22. David J. Rothman, *Politics and Power: The United States Senate 1869-1901* (Cambridge, Mass., 1966; Atheneum edn., New York, 1969), p. 45.

23. Samuel F. Emmons to George F. Becker, April 26, 1883, Becker Papers, Box 15, Manuscript Division, Library of Congress (henceforth LC).

24. Grove Karl Gilbert to William Morris Davis, June 13, 1893, Harvard Geographical Institute Papers, Houghton Library, Harvard University.

25. Thomas Corwin Mendenhall, Autobiographical Notes, VI, 36-46, Center for History and Philosophy of Physics, American Institute of Physics.

26. J.W. Powell to George F. Becker, April 29, 1884, Becker Papers, Box 15, LC.

27. Diary of Edward M. Gallaudet, March 30, 1881, Gallaudet Papers, LC.

28. Clarence King to Daniel C. Gilman, February 27, 1885, Gilman Papers, The Johns Hopkins University Library; Grove K. Gilbert to William H. Holmes, February 12, 1880, Holmes, "Random Records," National Collection of Fine Arts Library, SI.

29. Hay to Mrs. Adams, November 14, 1881, Theodore F. Dwight Papers, folder labeled John Hay to HA & Mrs. HA, 1881-1886, Massachusetts Historical Society.

30. Baird to A. Agassiz, June 9, 1883, Museum of Comparative Zoology Achives, Baird Folder, Harvard University; Tarleton H. Bean to William J. Rhees, August 10, 1883, Rhees Collection, RH 2714, Box 51, Henry E. Huntington Library and Art Gallery (henceforth HEHL).

31. Kip Ross, "The First Four Years," *Cosmos Club Bulletin*, XIII (March, 1960), 3; *The Twenty-Fifth Anniversary of the Cosmos Club*, pp. 68-71.

32. Pertinent here is the recent discussion of intuition and the writing of cultural history appearing in, Morse Peckham, "Darwinism and Darwinisticism," *Darwin*, ed. Philip Appleman (New York, 1970), pp. 387-388.

33. First Annual Report of the U. S. Geological Survey, in Edward Salisbury Dana et al., *A Century of Scence in America, with Special Reference to the American Journal of Science, 1818-1918* (New Haven, Conn., 1918), pp. 201-202; for his own part King "had incorporated the West into the realm of academic science," William H. Goetzmann, *Exploration and Empire: The Explorer and the Scientist in the Winning of the American West* (New York, 1966), p. 466.

34. Richard A. Bartlett, *Great Surveys of the American West* (Norman, Okla., 1962), pp. 373-376; Thomas G. Manning, *Government in Scence: The U. S. Geological Survey, 1867-1894* (Lexington, Ky., 1967), pp. 1-32; George P. Merrill, *The First Of Hundred Years of American Geology* (New Haven, Conn., 1924, New York, 1964), pp. 500-552; Howard D. Kramer, "The Scientist in the West, 1870-1880," *Pacific Historical Review,* XII (September, 1943), 239-251.

35. J. D. Whitney, "Geographical and Geological Surveys," *North American Review,* CXXI (July and October, 1875), 37-85, 270-314; Whitney was well versed in how government surveys could suddenly be abolished once they lost public favor, having had his own California State Geological Survey scuttled by the legislature the year before, Gerald D. Nash, "The Conflict Between Pure and Applied Science in Nineteenth-Century Public Policy: The California State Geological Survey, 1860-1874," *Isis,* LIV (June, 1963), 217-228.

36. U. S., Congress, *Index to the Miscellaneous Documents of the House . . .,* 46th Congress, 1st Session, 1879, Misc. Document 7, I, 6-8; The National Academy's role in consolidation is summarized in Frederick W. True (ed.), *A History of the First Half-Century of the National Academy of Sciences, 1863-1913.*

37. U. S., *Congressional Record,* 45th Congress, 3rd Session, 1879, VIII, Part 2, 1282.

38. *Ibid.* 218.

39. *Ibid.,* Part 7, 1211; the motives of congressmen opposing the Powell plan are thoughtfully analyzed in Goetzmann, *Exploration and Empire.* pp. 587-588; Manning, *Government in Science.* pp. 46-54.

40. *Ibid.,* Part 2, 1202; Henry Nash Smith, "Clarence King, John Wesley Powell, and the Establishment of the United States Geological Survey," *Mississippi Valley Historical Review,* XXXIV (June, 1947), 37-58.

41. In the judgement of the historian of the arid region Powell's analyses and recommendations "were the most intelligent and comprehensive that had been made, and they have not been surpassed since," Walter Prescott Webb, *The Great*

Plains (New York, 1931; Universal Library edn., n.d.), p. 422; for a more recent appraisal of Powell's impact on western historiography see, William Coleman, "Science and Symbol in the Turner Hypothesis," *American Historical Review*, LXXII (October, 1966), 28-29, 41-42.

42. Frank H. Cushing to [?] Turner, May 15, 1879, Cushing Papers, Southwest Museum Library.

43. Dall, *Baird*, p. 397; milder hints that the Cosmos Club must have had something to do with the creation of the Survey appear in William Culp Darrah, *Powell of the Colorado* (Princeton, N. J., 1951), pp. 247-248 and Goetzmann, *Exploration and Empire*, p. 591.

44. A valuable insight into the distinction between influence and power appears in David Grimsted, "Rioting in Its Jacksonian Setting," *American Historical Review*, LXXVII (April, 1972), 393, n.76.

45. Manning, *Government in Science*, p. 10; A. J. Liebling, "Annals of Crime: The American Golconda," *New Yorker*, XVI (November 16, 1940), 49-62; James D. Hague, "Memorabilia," *Clarence King Memoirs* (New York, 1904), pp. 396-400; Thurman Wilkins, *Clarence King: A Biography* (New York, 1958), pp. 158-172; Wallace Stengner, *Beyond the Hundredth Meridian: John Wesley Powell and the Second Opening of the West* (Boston, 1954), pp. 54-57; Darrah, *Powell*, pp. 128-129.

46. In later years a colleague wrote of King: "It was his personal charm and captivating speech that won for him an immediate and enduring success. Senators, representatives and government officials of every grade became at once his admiring friends. Fessenden, of Maine, after an evening's companionship with King at Sam Hooper's genial dinner-table, was himself almost persuaded to be a scientist, and professed his conversion in saying, 'if I were not United States Senator I would be United States Geologist,' " Hauge, *King Memoirs*, p. 382.

47. Military reconnaissances traditionally gave short shrift to exploration and conservation, both of which loomed larger than ever before in post-1865 conceptions of the trans-Mississippi west. As the historian of this subject has written: "Nearly to a man every Topographical Officer from Stephen H. Long onward had described the plains west of the 100th meridian as being of little value to a civilization largely agrarian in its basic economic activity. To them the plains country formed a barrier to progress." William H. Goetzmann, *Army Exploration in the American West, 1803-1863* (New Haven, Conn., 1959), pp. 415-416; "perhaps the climax of the War Department's geological effort came in

1859 . . . ." Manning, *Government in Science*, p. 2.

48. Bartlett, *Great Surveys,* pp. 333-372; the House Appropriations Committee's refusal to fund further surveys "was really a vote of no condifidence in Wheeler's work, and it marked the beginning of the end of large-scale army exploration in the West," Goetzmann, *Exploration and Empire,* p. 485; General A. A. Humphreys, Chief of Engineers, submitted his resignation to the National Academy and the Philosophical Society when he saw that the special committee appointed to study western surveys was composed of geologists and therefore stacked against topography, A. A. Humphreys to Theodore N. Gill, and Humphreys to Simon Newcomb, December 31, 1878, Philosophical Society of Washington Archives, United States Naval Research Laboratory.

49. Bartlett, *Great Surveys,* pp. 3-120; Manning, *Government in Science,* p. 15; Goetzmann, *Exploration and Empire,* pp. 495-529; for an incisive critique of Hayden's Survey see Jules Marcou to Hayden, January 27, 1874, in Merrill, *First One Hundred Years,* pp. 721-722.

50. Bartlett, *Great Surveys,* p. 20; J. P. Lesley, "Obituary Notice of Ferdinand Vandevere Hayden," *Proceedings of the American Philosophical Society,* XXV (January 20, 1888), 61; Charles A. White, "Memoir of Ferdinand Vandevere Hayden, 1839 [sic] -1887," *National Academy of Sciences Biographical Memoirs,* III (1895), 395-413; *Time Exposure: The Autobiography of William Henry Jackson* (New York, 1940), pp. 186-187; for Hayden's appreciation of untamed nature see Roderick Nash, *Wilderness and the American Mind* (New Haven, Conn., 1967), pp. 111-113.

51. Quoted in Frances Williams Binkley, "The Hayden Survey" (unpublished M.A. thesis, Department of History, University of Colorado, 1945), p. 61.

52. Nathan Reingold (ed.), *Science in Nineteenth-Century America: A Documentary History* (New York, 1964), p. 238; for more on "spectacular entrepeneurs" in paleontology see, Francis C. Haber, "Sidelights on American Science as Revealed in the Hyatt Autograph Collection," *Maryland Historical Magazine,* XLVI (December, 1951), 233-256; Charles Schuchert and Clara Mae LeVene, *O. C. Marsh: Pioneer in Paleontology* (New Haven, Conn., 1940), pp. 261-267; Henry Fairfield Osborn, *Cope: Master Naturalist . . .* (Princeton, N. J., 1931), pp. 177-273.

53. Julius E. Hilgard to Othniel C. Marsh, November 28, 1878, Marsh Letterbooks, Peabody Museum Library, Yale University; Ferdinand V. Hayden to Spencer F. Baird, Septmber 18 and 20, 1878, Baird Personal Papers, SI Archives.

54. O. C. Marsh to Rutherford B. Hayes, January 14, 1879, Hayes Papers, Rutherford B. Hayes Library (henceforth RBHL).

55. Clarence King to Daniel C. Gilman, January 15, 1879, Gilman Papers, The Johns Hopkins University Library; King was an old hand at using his irresistable charm to win choice government positions. In 1867, at the age of twenty-four, he induced Congress and the War Department to approve the 40th Parallel Survey and, through personal efforts, secured the directorship for himself. In bidding him adieu Secretary of War Stanton said: "Now, Mr. King, the sooner you get out of Washington the better   you are entirely too young to be seen about town with this appointment in your pocket   there are four major-generals who want your place." Quoted in Wilkins, *King*, p. 96. Small wonder that even Henry Adams stood in awe of King.

56. William   Dean Howells to Rutherford B. Hayes, and Elinor Howells to Lucy Webb Hays, January 4, 1879, Hayes Papers, RBHL; her father's letter is reprinted in Mildred Howells (ed.), *Life in Letters of William Dean Howells* (Garden City, N. Y., 1928), I, 261-262.

57. James Dwight Dana to Clarence King, January 7, 1879, Hayes Papers, RBHL; the battle of the testimonials is described in Manning, *Government in Science*, pp. 56-58.

58. Denys P. Myers, "Women and the Club," *Cosmos Club Bulletin*, XI (October, 1958), 2-5.

59. J. S. Billings, "Four Hundredth Meeting," *Bulletin of the Philosophical Society of Washington*, XII (1892-1894), 550-551.

60. Newcomb, *The Twenty-Fifth Anniversary of the Cosmos Club*, p. 34.

61. *Ibid.*, p. 34.

62. B. F. Stevens to T. F. Dwight, February 15, February 22, and May 22, 1879, Dwight Papers, folder labeled 1868-1879, Massachusetts Historical Society.

63. John S. Billings to Spencer F. Baird, December 3, 1878, Baird Personal Papers, SI Achives; Simon Newcomb to John S. Billings, December 3, 1883, Newcomb Papers, Box 5, LC; Edward S. Holden to William J. Rhees, August 30, 1879, Rhees Collection, RH 3323, Box 48, HEHL; *The Twenty-Fifth Anniversary of the Cosmos Club*, p. 89; for details about Howgate's escapade see Joseph M. Hawes, "The Signal Corps and Its Weather Service, 1870-1890," *Military*

Affairs, XXX (Summer, 1966), 74; and Donald R. Whitnah, *A History of the United States Weather Bureau* (Urbana, Ill., 1961), p. 46.

64. Hay and King used stationery with a five of hearts in the upper lefthand corner. Henry Adams was addressed as "The Heart of Hearts," King as "The Vagrant Heart," and Marian Adams as "Our Lady of Lafayette Square," See King to Adams, December 31, 1881, Box 7, folder labeled "To HA from various persons, 1861-1891," Hay to Mrs. Adams, November 14, 1881, Box 7, folder labeled "John Hay to HA & Mrs. HA, 1881-1886," Hay to Adams, January 3, 1884, *ibid.,* Dwight Papers, Massachusetts Historical Society; Constance McLaughlin Green, *The Church on Lafayette Square: A History of St. John's Church, Washington, D. C., 1815-1970* (Washington, D. C., 1970), pp. 49-67; Randall Bond Truett (ed.), *Washington, D. C.: A Guide to the Nation's Capital* (Washington, D. C., 1942; Hastings House revised edition, New York, 1968), pp. 250-259.

65. Hal M. Smith, "Historic Washington Homes," *Records of the Columbia Historical Society,* XI (Washington, D. C., 1908), 243-267; Gist Blair, "Lafayette Square," *ibid.,* XXVIII (Washington, D. C., 1926), 133-173; Spaulding, *Cosmos Club,* pp. 2-10; Ernest Samuels, *Henry Adams: The Middle Years* (Cambridge, Mass., 1958), pp. 143-180; Tyler Dennett, *John Hay: From Poetry to Politics* (New York, 1933), pp. 156-167.

66. *The Twenty-Fifth Anniversary of the Cosmos Club* pp. 142-155; Kip Ross, "The First Twenty-Five Years," *Cosmos Club Bulletin,* XIX (May, 1966), 4.

67. F. W. Clarke, "Science in Politics," *Popular Science Monthly,* XXVI (March, 1885), 577.

68. Albert Williams, Jr. to George F. Becker, December 3, 1883, Becker Papers, Box 15, LC.

69. Powell and Holden to Holmes, November 18, 1878, Holmes, "Random Records," National Collection of Fine Arts Library, SI.

70. Thomas C. Mendenhall, Autobiographical Notes, V, 151-152, Mendenhall Papers, American Institute of Physics.

71. Goetzmann, *Exploration and Empire,* p. 579.

5

The Minute Seed

A perceptive Washingtonian, scanning the special notices column in the *Evening Star* of Friday, February 7, 1879, would have found intriguing the news that the Capital was about to become the home of a new scientific body. "Many persons interested in American archaeology have expressed a desire for an organization in this city . . . to promote study and diffuse knowledge upon the subject," read the announcement. A meeting had been called for the following Monday in the Regent's Room of the Smithsonian Institution, and all those willing to join such an association were asked to attend. This general invitation ended with the names of three valuable contributors to the formation of Washington's intellectual community: Colonel Garrick Mallery, Professor Otis T. Mason, and Dr. Joseph Meredith Toner.[1]

Mallery would always look back upon 1879 as a significant point in his life. That was when, in his forty-eighth year, he helped found the Anthropoligical Society of Washington; and it was then that he mustered out of the regular army and accepted a position in Powell's recently created Bureau of Ethnology. The Colonel had not sought retirement. It had come as the result of wounds suffered in the Civil War which eventually rendered him unfit for further service. In fact, it is reasonable to suppose that had his discharge not been forced he would have remained a career officer, for he thrived in the military. When Fort Sumpter fell, Mallery was a fast rising Philadelphia attorney. He had graduated from Yale and then taken his law degree at the University of Pennsylvania. Barely thirty at the war's outbreak, he was already prosperous and generally well thought of, and his future seemed glorious. These considerations deterred him not at all. He literally dashed to the colors and volunteered as a private. In June of 1861 he was made a Captain of Infantry in the 71st Pennsylvania, and over the course of the next four years rose to the rank of Brevet-Colonel. Duty with the Signal Service, and the Geographical and Geological Survey of the Rocky Mountain Region followed, before he finally succumbed to lingering disabilities.[2]

The army's loss proved to be a gain for science. Even before launching another career Mallery had begun studying Indian culture and publishing his findings. When he joined the Bureau of Ethnology, his novitiate was behind him and he was prepared to turn his attention to problems of fundamental importance. Mallery wanted to know how Indians acquired and transmitted ideas. The answer seemed to lie in a thorough understanding of sign language and pictography. He therefore undertook the "collection and collation" of all symbols, gestures, and facial expressions that were language representations.[3] Aided by an assortment of cavalry officers, missionaries, doctors, land officials, and Indian agents scattered over the western parts of the United States and Canada who furnished descriptive lists of "sign talk," he produced several comprehensive monographs that were published by the Smithsonian Institution. These reports rank with the notable accomplishments of the Bureau's early period.

Mallery's work reflects an affinity for North American natives, showing why he felt at home among the canyons and praries of the west. Even so, in certain quarters his motives were suspect, and it was held that, as an ethnologist, he was exploiting the Indian in order to protect his own job. Some of his contemporaries who were engaged in "civilizing" missions contended that ethnologists had no real sympathy for Indians, and that they wanted to keep them segregated on reservations and hold back Indian advancement so they could be studied in their natural state. Captain Pratt, who founded the Carlisle Indian School in the same year that the Bureau of Ethnology was established, insisted that the education of Indians could proceed only after they had been "isolated from their savagery."[4] However, obstacles were constantly being strewn in the path of acculturation by ethnologists and their ilk at the Bureau of Indian Affairs. Pratt saw in the "Bureau oligarchy" *a deus ex machina* to "keep the Indians from the opportunities and environment of civilized life," because Indian citizenship would render the Bureau obsolete.[5]

It is true that a frequently used justification for the Bureau of Ethnology was that it existed to gather information about cultures that were rapidly disappearing, thus leaving precious little time in which to carry out meaningful ethnological research. The Bureau's spirtual lineage can be traced back to the admonition voiced by Thomas Jefferson several generations earlier:

It is to be lamented . . . that we have suffered so many of the Indian tribes
already to extinguish, without our having previously collected and deposited
in the records of literature, the general rudiments at least of the languages
they spoke.[6]

Using this same idiom, John Wesley Powell took advantage of the sense of
urgency surrounding the "vanishing savage" to gain support for salvaging
and recording cultural data.[7] Yet the Bureau could also be defended as an
instrument of justice for the Indian. When Powell, on behalf of the
National Academy of Sciences, appealed for government backing of ethnology, he seized the opportunity to call for a more enlightened approach
to the "Indian problem." It did not take Wounded Knee to awaken Powell
to the fact that, "The blunders we have made and the wrongs we have
inflicted upon the Indians have been cruel and inexcusable, except on the
ground of our ignorance."[8] Powell's humanitarian views—and lack of scientific neutrality—were shared by Mallery. He also wrote compassionately
about Indians, and desired the immediate assimilation of a "race entrusted
to our national honor, which may readily and with no long delay, become
a valuable element in our motley community."[9]

Mallery's bureau reports exhibit creative brilliance, helping to explain
why he was so highly esteemed by Washington's intellectual community.
The Colonel was also a man of personal charm. He possessed a keen sense
of humor and was an entertaining raconteur, qualities that made him
welcome in the most cultivated Lafayette Square salons. Recent acquaintances sometimes mistook his cynicism for surliness, yet Mallery had many
close friends, and those who wrote about him were struck by the fact that
he never lost his military bearing.[10] Perhaps it was his stern countenance,
or his erect carriage. At any rate he was an imposing individual who gave
an impression of rugged manliness. With his strong visage, full moustache,
and pince-nez he had a look of determination not unlike Theodore
Roosevelt's. Doubtless both men would have found this comparison flat-
tering.,

The year 1879 had special meaning for Otis Tufton Mason. That date
was inscribed on his Ph.D. degree from Columbian University in Washington, where he was principal of the Preparatory School. At the time he
also worked as a collaborator in ethnology at the Smithsonian Institution.
In fact, the Smithsonian appears with such frequency in the life of Mason
that it is impossible to disconnect his achievements from the former's late
nineteenth century burgeoning activity.

Ever since boyhood Mason had found the Smithsonian irresistible. His earliest recollections of the place ran back to a day in the fifties, when he hiked sixteen miles up the Potomac from his family's farm in Virginia to Washington. As soon as he entered the city he felt drawn toward the Smithsonian. Nearing the Mall he saw a large gathering of men and women in front of the reddish-brown sandstone building. Curiosity impelled him to join them and, before he knew it, he was swept upstairs with the rest of the crowd where Joseph Henry was giving a lecture. Over the years, as Mason pondered this experience, he came to regard it as an event of epochal proportions. And well he might, for once inside the Smithsonian he never really left.[11]

This institution also had a formative influence upon his scholarly life. It was Professor Henry who convinced him that biblical archeology, to which Mason had initially been attracted, was less important than studying North American Indian tribes. The Smithsonian thus set the course of Mason's career, and it was through the Smithsonian that Mason rose to eminence as the first real museum ethnologist in the United States. Being a professional placed him in very select company; hence his expertise was constantly in demand. In 1875, when the U. S. National Museum was bulging with ethnological specimens, Mason was prevailed upon to catalog and arrange the collection. He also edited anthropological papers for the Institution. In 1884, after he had already made a provisional classification of the collections, Mason was appointed Curator of the Department of Ethnology. By this chain of events the Smithsonian acquired another outstanding anthropologist and, in the process, added to its stature as a great locus of Indian study.[12]

Mason's position at the National Museum demanded all the ingenuity and skill he could muster in order to maintain the ever increasing collections made by the Bureau of Ethnology. Not only did he have charge of an enormous number of material objects, but he had to assemble them in a manner that would both enrich the Museum's public displays and make the collections usable for ethnologists doing research. He had to keep an eye on the Museum's role in professional investigation without losing sight of its responsibility to public entertainment and enlightenment.[13] So masterfully did this gentle man with the neatly trimmed beard perform his tasks that he became recognized as a leader in museum science. This was the period when the "National Cabinet of Curiosities" was being transformed into a comprehensive, instructive museum, and Mason's assistance proved vital to this endeavor.

Mason was also one of the most versatile anthropologists of his day, a fact that tells a great deal about his character and background. He had been raised in a household where such traits as wide-ranging intellectual curiosity, liberal education, community service, and social responsibility received every possible encouragement. John and Rachel Lincoln Mason, his parents, were transplanted New Hampshireites, having purchased in 1850 the mansion and 500 acres of "Woodlawn." This once fine estate adjacent to the Mount Vernon plantation had become dilapidated and overgrown, but the Mason's were not easily discouraged. They had come to Virginia for a dual purpose: to promote their lumber business while building a free labor enclave, and working in concert with a band of anti-slavery Quakers they were notably successful. The Mason's founded the Woodlawn Baptist Church. They helped to start the Woodlawn Elementary School almost twenty-five years before the Virginia Public School System began. They formed the Woodlawn Farmers Club for the study of scientific agriculture and the reading of papers. And they were chiefly responsible for the Woodlawn Housekeeping Club, Woodlawn Fruit Growers Association, and the Woodlawn Horse Company. All these institutions were racially integrated, and the Mason's aided a number of former slaves in becoming prosperous farmers. Otis was twelve when his venture began, and his progress into young manhood was shaped by participation in the development of a community. At the same time he came to appreciate how his father — whose 300 volume library included works on history, economics, theology, literature, geography, science, and political theory — continuously stressed a practical orientation of knowledge.[14]

These impressions remained with Otis Mason throughout his professional career, accounting partially for his role in the formation of Washington's intellectual community, and helping to explain his predisposition toward the popularization of science. Although he defined anthropology broadly, and considered every aspect of man's natural history grist for the practitioner's mill, his writing never suffered because of it.[15] He published widely in the field of aboriginal material culture, and according to a colleague, "had the rare gift of presenting the scientific data in such a style and manner that his works can be read with profit and pleasure by men and women of intelligence in all vocations."[16]

Here was a truly indomitable man whose vitality and capacity for sustained exertion bordered on the phenomenal. Mason's admirers liked to recount how, when he was past sixty, he suffered a stroke that paralyzed his right hand. Undaunted by this affliction he promptly taught himself to write left handed and, in a matter of weeks, was able to resume his normal schedule of constant work. This glimpse into Mason's character makes plausible his promotion to the head Curatorship of Anthropology at an age when most men are preparing for retirement. Advancing years had little effect on his activities, and for over a quarter century Otis T. Mason was a bulwark of the Smithsonian Institution, just as he was of the Anthropological Society of Washington.

Unlike Mallery and Mason, Joseph Meredith Toner had no direct connection with ethnology, but this did not mean that his name was foreign to Washington's intellectuals. Of the three principal founders of the Society Dr. Toner undoubtedly was the best known. His forte was encouraging medical research, and for many years he had figured prominently in the advancement of American medicine. There was an element of irony in this because, even though he was a respected physician, his own work was not singular. "Perhaps the leading characteristic of his pursuit of scientific subjects was assiduity rather than originality," admitted a friend.[17] Such individuals are always needed; after the Civil War Toner was invaluable to the development of Washington's scientific community. So firm was his commitment to establishing institutions and inducements for research that he allowed his practice to dwindle away to a handful of personal acquaintances, thus permitting himself to lavish all his attention on the promotion of scientific and literary activities.

His most famous effort along these lines was the Toner Lecture series, which he endowed and which was administered by the Smithsonian. Beginning in 1873, the Toner Lectures were delivered annually in Washington as original contributions to medical knowledge. Subsequently the papers were published in the *Smithsonain Miscellaneous Collections.* Toner also gave a medal to the school where he earned his M.D., Jefferson Medical College in Philadelphia. This was awarded each year to the student whose experiments and investigations showed the greatest originality. Another Toner Medal was one he presented to Georgetown University, which went to the graduate who was most proficient in science.

Toner's ample presence could always be found in the vanguard of programs aimed at improving public health and medical libraries, especially the Surgeon General's Library and the Library of the American Medical Association. His interest in public health stemmed from having worked to quell the Pittsburgh cholera epidemic of 1854; and the following year Norfolk's yellow fever epidemic. After those experiences preventive medicine became his specialty and he wrote numerous articles on infectious diseases. His concern about hygiene and municipal sanitation as major problems of modern industrial centers was remarkably prescient. He was an early proponent of summer fresh air camps for children of the urban poor.

Toner's obsession with libraries was understandable, considering that he was one of the country's greatest bibliophiles. The Librarian of Congress recalled that Toner "was for forty years a familiar figure in nearly all the bookstores, book auctions, and junk shops of this and of some other cities, and though reputed a close buyer, he expended largely in amassing medical, historical, and biographical literature."[18] The result was a huge personal library of both printed and manuscript material. When he began the collection his major interest was medicine, and he acquired books, pamphlets, and periodicals dealing with the medical profession. This led to a more specialized interest in American doctors, which in turn, led to American biography up to the Revolution. The final stage in building his library, and the one which consumed his later years, was gathering everything he could that had been written by and about George Washington. Thus, he put together a treasury of Washingtoniana which still has value. In 1878, imbued with the spirit of philanthropy, he offered his library to the doctors of Chicago upon the condition that they provide a fireproof structure in which to house it. Similar propositions had already been made to the medical professions in Pittsburgh and St. Louis. But in each case raising the money proved an impossible task, so in 1882 he gave the entire collection—by this time numbering twenty-seven thousand volumes—to the Library of Congress.[19]

The doctor's overweight did not derive from indolence. In addition to book collecting he wrote continuously on a broad range of subjects (a life long bachelor, his first book was *Maternal Instinct*). It is hard to find a Washington hospital or an orphanage during this period that Toner did not either found or assist in some way, usually as the physician or a member of the board of directors. His affiliations with local and national associations were many, and he was elected President of the Medical Society of the District of Columbia (1870), the American Medical Association (1873), and the American Public Health Association (1874). These honors were fitting rewards for one who was extraordinarily generous with both his time and his talents.

These three men were already participating in local intellectual organizations at the time they called for the establishment of an anthropological society. Mallery was active in both the Literary and Philosophical Societies, while Mason was a Philosophical Society member and Toner a bellwether in the Literary Society. Only a few months earlier the three had helped found the Cosmos Club. Now they were seeking to expand the network of societies to include the growing number of Washingtonians who were anxious to delve into the absorbing problems concerning primitive life on their continent.

Word of this venture proved sufficiently exciting to attract twenty-five men to the meeting scheduled for February 10, 1879. Dr. Toner served as temporary president, and under his approving eye the organization was formally established. There was considerable discussion concerning the breadth of interests to be pursued. Should the Society embrace all that was relevant to the origins, nature, and history of man in America, or would it be better to limit itself to American antiquities? The founders boldly chose the first alternative, thereby deciding not to confine their activities to archeology as had been originally suggested. With this matter resolved, and after Mason, Mallery, Toner, and Willis De Hass had been appointed to draft a constitution, the Anthropological Society of Washington adjourned until February seventeenth.[20]

Though they could not have fully comprehended it at the time, the founders were living through a critical period in the history of anthropology, and what they were doing would have an important bearing upon the development of their profession. They themselves hardly constituted a professional group of practicing anthropologists. Only Mason, Mallery, De Hass, Frank Hamilton Cushing, and P. W. Norris were engaged in work relating to anthropology and ethnology, leaving eighty per cent of the Society far outside that field of inquiry that they promised to "promote study and diffuse knowledge upon." With occupations ranging from physician, to banker, to naval officer, and to civil engineer, none actually taught anthropology and none held a doctorate in the field. So far as professionalization on the national scene was concerned, Spencer Baird was the lone founder in the National Academy of Sciences (John Wesley Powell, technically not a founder but the Soceity's first president, would be tapped by the National Academy in 1880).[21] Powell was also vice-president of the Natural History Section of the AAAS, and in 1879 was elected chairman of its Permanent Subsection of Anthropology for the 1880 meeting. At the same time Mallery was a AAAS member, while Baird, George Brown Goode, Mason, and Ward had been elevated to the more prestigious category of AAAS fellows.[22] More interesting, though, is the fact that·so few of the Society's early members had professional credentials, and that this did not seem to bother them.

Even the practitioners showed little sense of professional awareness or special identity. Except for Garrick Mallery and Otis Mason, no one called himself an ethnologist for purposes of classification in the 1879 City Directory.[23] And that designation must not have been given too deliberately, for when the Census of 1880 was taken Mason filled in "Prin lcipal]

Prep School" as his "Profession."[24] Thus the Society failed an elementary test of professional organization. "Growth of self-awareness, probably constitutes the most important element contributing to professionalization," argues Geoffrey Millerson in his recent examination of the subject. "Until members of an occupation realize their collective existence as a group, then movement toward professionalization cannot begin."[25] If occupational cohesiveness and self-conscious definition are valid guides, then the popular impression of the Society as an association of gentlemen rather than a professional guild was correct. This was the description it received in the local press,[26] and, as one of the classic studies of the professions makes clear, "public recognition can hardly be accorded to a group that has not discovered itself."[27]

Despite its lack of professionalism in consciousness or composition, the Society displayed certain tendencies that were unmistakably professional. Its study was broken down into four sections (somatology, sociology, philology, and philosophy and psychology), reflecting the structural lines of the AAAS, acknowledging the disciplinary specializations of modern scientific knowledge, and anticipating the academic professionalization that would characterize the university system in the twentieth century.[28] Occupationally, the Society's leaders tended to be individuals who clustered around the Smithsonian Institution and related agencies and bureaus, and this afforded a framework within which professional growth could occur. According to the constitution it was the explicit duty of "all members to seek to increase and perfect the materials for anthropological study in the national institutions at Washington."[29] As these institutions gained in stature, so did their staff members come to be recognized as budding professionals. This was particularly true for those associated with the Bureau of Ethnology, which by design had the closest of relationships with the Society. Powell was the prime mover in both, causing them to progress in tandem; once they were underway, anthropology was on the road toward becoming a profession. Indeed, a professional in 1879 may be defined as one who was employed by the Bureau and for whom the Bureau made possible a lifetime career in anthropology. Its staff constituted, "in effect, the first full-time professional anthropologists."[30] By extension, some of this status adhered to their organization, placing the Anthropological Society of Washington temporarily at the forefront of professionalization.

Interestingly, however, its spokesmen bent over backward drawing attention to its amateur attributes. Every opportunity was seized to encourage laymen and to reap the dividends of anthropology's wide appeal. "Anthropology, or what may be considered the natural history of man, is at present the most popular branch of science," Joseph Henry had observed in 1877. "It absorbs a large share of public attention and many original investigators are assiduously devoted to it."[31] "Public attention" and "original investigators": here was a vital partnership involving friends of science and practitioners of science, a variation on the theme which Howard S. Miller finds running throughout the Gilded Age. The Society represented yet another version of enterprise stemming from "a productive partnership between public and private, corporate and individual effort."[32] In this case the partners were fledgling professionals and interested laymen, and in promoting the relationship the Society not only threw open its doors to amateurs, it eagerly hailed inside all likely prospects for membership.

There were too few practitioners in 1879 to sustain a purely professional organization anyway. Washington probably counted more persons actually doing anthropological and ethnological work than any other center of investigation, due to the related activities of the Smithsonian's national museum, the Bureau of the Census, and the federal geological surveys. Still the numbers were small, as evidenced by the modest size of the Bureau of Ethnology. When Powell set up his first office at the Smithsonian he requisitioned space for only twenty-five people, and this total included a letter clerk, a copyist, three messengers, and the watchman.[33] Even so, there must have been many empty desks because his budget reports during the first five years show a staff of between twelve and twenty, several of whom were field workers.[34] By happily admitting amateurs Powell and the handful of practitioners proved themselves realists. Organizational necessity was not their sole consideration, however, for they saw in inclusiveness more leasting virtues.

An open society would attract more friends for science, which meant a firmer base of support for itself, for the Bureau, and for anthropology. Mason applauded the absence of professional distinction in the Society because its influence could thereby be extended to reach various levels of the community. And in so doing the literate public would be guaranteed not only access to knowledge, but an opportunity to join in scientific quests.[35] "Who may be an anthropologist?" he asked rhetorically. "Every man, woman, and child that has sense and patience to observe, and that can honestly record the thing observed."[36] Early meetings justified his confidence in a paraprofessional organization as soldiers sat next to scientists, and educators beside bureaucrats. The Anthropological Society had insinuated itself into the culture of the Capital City. Mason subsequently ascribed this initial success to getting the "doctors, lawyers, architects, engineers, clergy, Rabbis, everybody interested. That is the way I greased the wheels of our now flourishing Anthropological Society.[37] Conversely, the Society's favor among persons of divergent backgrounds and occupations helped broadcast the appeal of anthropology throughout Washington.

But what of its potential for contributing to anthropology when so few of its members had proven competence in the field? Once again an apparent deficiency, upon closer inspection, turned into an asset, and there is nothing to indicate that the founders suffered any qualms about proceeding with their venture because the Society was composed mainly of amateurs. The annals of early anthropology and ethnology glowed with the achievements of paraprofessionals. Captain Meriwether Lewis and Lieutenant William Clark, for example, were scantily prepared to comprehend the wonders of ethnography in the trans-Mississippi wilderness. Yet they knew enough to collect much valuable data, and proved themselves first rate field researchers, particularly Lewis, who undertook the expedition equipped with detailed lists of questions to ask Indians, and applied anthropology "in its most modern sense."[38] This story of interested laymen doing pioneer work in linguistics, ethnology, archeology, and physical anthropology, and of making worthwhile additions to the storehouse of anthropological knowledge, had been repeated time after time.

During the period when the Anthropological Society of Washington was being founded Lewis Henry Morgan was the doyen of American anthropologists. His accomplishments were legion: he had established the Anthropology Section of the American Association for the Advancement of Science; published *Ancient Society;* attained membership in the National Academy of Sciences; and inspired numerous younger men, such as John Wesley Powell, who lauded his "record of facts previously unknown to science."[39] Morgan also embodied the tradition of the amateur in anthropology. He was neither specially trained nor a full time worker in the discipline.

"The circumstances which led to his interest in ethnology," wrote an old colleague, "are worthy of record and serve to illustrate the character and tastes of the man."[40] They also serve to reveal something of the haphazard progress of anthropological science in the antebellum period. As a young lawyer Morgan was one of the main founders of the Order of the Gordian Knot, a fraternal body based on Greek myths with chapters that met in the abandoned Masonic lodges of a dozen towns across rural western New York. In 1843, at the annual summer conclave held in Aurora,

Morgan persuaded the five hundred members that it would be appropriate to replace classical forms with Iroquois customs. Accordingly the association became the Grand Order of the Iroquois and the Aurora Lodge turned into the Cayuga Tribe, with Morgan as its chief. His first duty was to acquire information about Iroquois ceremonies and ritual. Soon he became interested in institutions, the structure of tribal organizations, and broader patterns of Indian culture. It was fitting that this happened to be the take-off period in the development of American anthropology, for suddenly Morgan's perfunctory attempt to find out something about Indian lore had blossomed into a full fledged study of ethnology.[41]

The tale of Morgan's accidental entry into anthropology is well known. Less familiar is the fact that his monumental studies were sandwiched between a legal practice, business enterprises, and dabbling in politics. Even his early investigations among the Senecas were intertwined with lobbying on their behalf in Washington and Albany to forestall their removal west of the Mississippi.[42] But even though Morgan was unable to devote all his time to science, "like a colossus he strode in every field of anthropology, influencing his generation with his burning enthusiasm and agreeable disposition."[43] His influence prevailed over the next generation as well, as the founders of the Anthropological Society launched their organization in the same spirit of fervor and congeniality.

In substance these men went much farther toward raising anthropology to a higher stage of professional development. The generations of Morgan and Powell witnessed the decline of the amateur in science and the emergence of the professional. To modify Richard Hofstadter's famous generalization about the United States being born in the country and having moved to the city, American science was conceived by amateurs and adopted by professionals. Professionalization took hold in different sciences at different times, and under varying circumstances. With regard to anthropology, the eighties and nineties were key, for this era of government science and institution building in Washington formed the transition between the age of Morgan and the new anthropology of Franz Boas. If Morgan is associated with its birth, and Boas with its twentieth century maturation, then the period between may be considered the magic years of professional growth. When the Society was founded Morgan was sixty-one, Boas twenty-one, and Powell forty-five. This generational sequence symbolizes its pivotal position as an intermediate structure of professionalization, the crucial entity that Thomas S. Kunn has located between the stages of interested students of nature and full-fledged practitioners of a discipline.[44]

In 1879, American anthropology had not progressed far along "the route to normal science." It claimed no coherent tradition of research, no "body of intertwined theoretical and methodological belief that permits selection, evaluation, and criticism." Its "acquisition of a paradigm" lay in the future, and its "locus of professional commitment" was yet to be found.[45] To begin with there were actually very few anthropologists. Robert V. Bruce's recent study of distinguished American scientists finds exactly one who by 1876 was considered to have a field or major subfield in anthropology.[46] There had been but a single journal, *The Journal of the Anthropological Institute of New York* (1871-1872), and it was discontinued after just one number.[47] Virtually all anthropologists were self-taught during this preacademic period. Daniel Garrison Brinton became America's first recognized teacher (his title was Professor of Archeology and Linguistics) in 1886 at the University of Pennsylvania; that was when graduate training began, on a limited scale, with Clark University awarding the first anthropology Ph.D. in 1892.[48] The lack of professional consciousness and occupational identity on the part of Washington's working anthropologists highlighted the larger truth that most practitioners still earned their livings in other fields. As a consequence, and because anthropology had not appropriated a systematized, esoteric body of knowledge that would signal its arrival among the scientific professions,[49] it lacked the integrity and authority to legitimize, to set and judge qualifications for practice, to certify, and to sanction a code of guild procedures. The only prerequisite for the host of dabblers was a curiosity about the physical and mental life of mankind—hardly a rigid restriction.[50] "America has no *science* of ethnology or archaeology," complained Cushing in 1876: "... every boor who has correctly or incorrectly described an arrow head or a simple mound is at once considered an archaeologist and styles himself, 'Professor.'"[51] This was redolent of Joseph Henry's lament thirty years before, that "every man who can burn prosphorous in oxygen and exhibit a few experiments to a class of young ladies is called a man of science,"[52] and signified the distance separating anthropology in the seventies from true professional status.

Not until the end of the nineteenth century would professionalization be secured, and then because anthropology finally had taken on the characgeristics of a formal discipline. By that time definite lines of specialization were being drawn, autonomy in terms of occupation, methods, assumptions, concepts, and a body of data was being achieved, nationally recognized standards of performance were gaining acceptance—in short, anthropology was being shaped to the norms of a modern university discipline.[53]

In the meantime, however, it owed a considerable degree of what "self-definition" it possessed to the Anthropological Society of Washington.[54]

The Society's constitution, adopted at the second meeting, both confirmed what had already taken place and provided an instrument of government for future operations. It stated that the main business of the Anthropological Society of Washington was to "encourage the study of the Natural History of Man, especially with reference to America," and that the members "shall be persons who are interested in Anthropology." Thus the founders' preference for a relatively non-restrictive organization as to who could belong and what they would do was written into the official document. However, controlling power within the Society was not fractionated, it was thoroughly centralized. There would be a Council of fifteen members, later known as the Board of Managers, in which was vested absolute authority over all the Society's affairs. Elected annually by the whole membership, it was to consist of the president, vice-presidents who also were *ex officio* chairmen of the Society's four sections, corresponding and recording secretaries, the treasurer, the curator, and six other members designated as councilors. This directory passed on nominations for membership in the Society, handled its finances, received communications, had responsibility for programs and publications, and was empowered to call special meetings. In short, the members of the Council "transacted all business of the Society, save their own elections."[55]

It made little difference how members of the Council were chosen because the same men tended to be perennial office holders. The offices that they held might change from year to year, but their elections to the Council seem to have been *pro forma*. Throughout the Society's early history, when the attrition rate was low anyway, what few Council replacements were needed were drawn almost invariably from the slate of incumbents. Between 1880, when the terms of the first officers expired, and 1885 there were ninety Council positions that had to be filled, yet only twenty-three men filled them. A further breakdown of this figure reveals that seventeen of these went onto the Council at the councilor level. In other words, roughly seventy-five per cent of the changes took place at the bottom of the power structure, which made for remarkable continuity in the higher offices. Powell was elected president every year but one, when illness forced him to relinquish the office to Mallery (Powell still served as a vice-president). Walter J. Hoffman, Colonel Franklin A. Seely, and Lester Frank Ward were on the Council year after year. Mallery, the author of the constitution and by-laws, Mason, and Powell were never out of office. Thus the founders held sway and provided the stability that was more highly prized than dispersion of authority.[56]

The settled character of the Society's governing body acted as a counterweight against its lack of a permanent home. Without chambers of its own, or a fixed location for meetings, the Society was obliged to wander about the city accepting temporary quarters wherever they might be available. Unfortunately the early records of the Society fail to record where meetings were held, but the retrospections of an old member and former president leave the impression of as nomadic an existence as that of some of the peoples they were studying. Society gatherings shifted from the Regents' Room of the Smithsonian, to the National Medical College, to the Library of the Army Medical Museum, and eventually to the lecture hall of Columbian University. In April 1887, as was the case with so many societies of this kind, it accepted the invitation to use the facilities of the Cosmos Club. There it remained, except for unusually large sessions which had to be transferred to places where more visitors could be accommodated. The Builders' Exchange Hall often was used for annual meetings where attendance might run as high as two hundred and fifty.[57]

An average of between fifty and sixty persons were on hand for regular meetings of the Society which occurred twice a month, on alternate Tuesday evenings, October through June. The main orders of business were the lectures and discussions that followed. Indeed these were the only items on the agenda that involved the Society as a whole. Minutes of preceding meetings were read and approved, donations were acknowledged, and new members were received all in a most perfunctory manner. The role of the general membership in operating the Society was clearly a passive one. Administrative matters were deliberated and decided upon by the Board of Managers which always convened separately one hour before regular meetings. By the time the rest of the Society gathered everything had been taken care of save the lectures for that evening—and these had to be approved by the Board of Managers prior to their presentation.[58]

The meticulous planning of programs and the seriousness with which lectures were regarded testifies to the importance of formal papers in the life of the Anthropological Society. These were its meat and drink; nothing was allowed to inhibit the speaker or distract the audience from partaking of the Society's intellectual offerings. At least two papers were given in an evening, so by disposing of routine affairs in a Board of Managers' meeting held in advance more time was provided for lectures and discussions. Similarly, it was not only expedient to run the Society this way, but by vesting absolute authority in the Board of Managers all but a handful of members were spared the often irksome tasks of administration. The result was that both the quality of lectures and the interest they commanded remained high. Anything less would have constituted a severe disappointment. Because the Society existed for the two-fold objective of disseminating knowledge and encouraging further study, and since this aim could best be accomplished through oral presentations which might subsequently be published, it was vital that the Society have superior lectures. If its biweekly programs were failures then the Anthropological Society would fail in its purpose— it was as simple as that.

Formal papers answered a definite need of the organization and in an immediate way they also provided intellectual stimulation for individual members. Less directly, they served to promote the new science of man. Through communications to the Society persons doing research were given a chance to test certain concepts and theories related to their work. During the Society's discussion sessions these notions would be criticized and debated by other students of the particular subjects. Finally, after further reflection and more systematic development, selected original lectures were prepared for publication. Society meetings served as a crucible for many noteworthy monographs of the 1880's dealing with archeology, ethnology, sociology, and psychology before they were put into finished form. Edward M. Gallaudet, founder and president of the National Deaf-Mute College, read his "How Shall the Deaf be Educated?" before it appeared in the *International Review* (December, 1881). Members of the Anthropological Society were the first to hear Cyrus Thomas's ideas about mound builders. Likewise, the study of Indian superstitions by Henry C. Yarrow was presented to the Society prior to publication in the *American Antiquarian and Oriental Journal* (January, 1882). Lester Frank Ward frequently spoke at meetings with several of his papers constituting chapters of *Dynamic Sociology.* [59]

Washington's Anthropological Society thus enjoyed the good fortune of being treated to an outstanding run of lectures. Also, it was blessed with a large number of men who were always eager to describe the fruits of their labors. Because lecturing afforded a means of gaining individual recognition, and since serials such as *Contributions to North American Ethnology,* the *Annual Report of the Bureau of Ethnology,* and the *Annual Report of the Board of Regents of the Smithsonian Institution* were willing to accept articles by members, it is no wonder that the Committee on Communications often received far more papers than it could possibly fit into a year of meetings. In 1893 W J McGee confessed that the Society was "almost embarrassed by the wealth of material for the present season, and will probably have to provide several special meetings . . . ." [60]

A more difficult problem was finding the best way of disseminating information about the pursuit of this increasingly popular science. Once again the Anthropolological Society was brought face to face with the dilemma that was inherent in its organization, namely how at the same time to serve a small group of incipient professionals and larger body of interested amateurs. In the case of the Society, this issue had been resolved by structuring the association so that anyone might belong while authority rested with a controlling elite. The matter of diffusing knowledge, however, could not be dealt with so easily. Practitioners needed a means for exchanging ideas and reporting their latest discoveries. Yet scientific periodicals had notoriously small circulations, a fact which militated against starting a journal of anthropology. The founders knew that an ill-starred venture could turn into an albatross leading the Society to destruction. Good sense cautioned not to be hasty about trying the stormy seas of scholarly publication. On the other hand, if the Society had no official voice its diffusion of knowledge would be hopelessly insular, and its effect upon anthropology outside of Washington practically nil. Individual members might publish their lectures, but these did not carry the imprimatur of the Anthropological Society. Prudence prevailed, and during the early years of its existence few heard from the Society as such, except those who attended its meetings.[61]

Considering this reluctance to become weighted down with the operation of a costly journal, it is understandable that the Society's initial publication was something less than ambitious. In 1882 Volume I of *Transactions of the Anthropological Society of Washington* appeared, a one hundred and forty-two page synopsis of the first three years of meetings. Included were a brief historical sketch, its constitution, names of members and officers for 1882, Powell's presidential address of that year, and an index. Obviously this did not leave much space for communications, which were merely listed or, at best, abstracted. The *Transactions* was made possible by the support of the Smithsonian Institution, which also published its contents, plus abstracts of papers read between March, 1879 and January, 1881 in the *Smithsonian Miscellaneous Collections* for 1883. The same format—and the same means of assistance—were repeated for two more volumes, enabling publication to continue through 1885. However, this was hardly satisfactory for announcing the activities of the Society and heralding the new truths discovered by its members.

Far more suitable was the *American Anthropologist* which produced its first number in January, 1888. Thereafter the journal was published on a regular quarterly schedule, a distinct improvement over the biennial appearances of the *Transactions*. This meant that members were receiving about eight times the quantity of matter as before, and in terms of quality the contrast was profound.

Ostensibly the *American Anthropologist* formed a continuation of the *Transactions*, but a glance at their respective contents reveals a world of difference. In the *Transactions* resumes of papers were usually limited to a few paragraphs, followed by transcripts of the discussions. The *American Anthropologist* contained full length articles of six to eight thousand words. These were often printed versions of lectures delivered at meetings, and to this extent the new publication was just as much an organ of the Anthropological Society as the *Transactions* had been. Also, the editorial board consisted of Society members and the Society's seal dominated the cover of every issue, leaving no doubt about who sponsored the *American Anthropologist*. But at the same time its orientation seemed less provincial.

Whereas the *Transactions* provided nothing more than truncated summaries of Washington meetings, the second publishing venture gave an impression of the national scope and professional maturity. It fulfilled what its title promised: an American journal of anthropology in the broadest sense. Beginning with Volume II, in 1889, its self-advertisement below the table of contents emphasized that "THE AMERICAN ANTHRO-POLOGIST . . . includes, but is not confined to, the Transactions of the Anthropological Society of Washington. . . ." It was as good as its word. There were notices of anthropology meetings throughout the United States and Europe, announcements of professional import such as the awarding of Ph.D.'s in anthropology and the introduction of anthropology courses at American universities, book reviews, quarterly bibliographies, and miscellaneous items of interest to professionals and laymen both within and outside of Washington. In substance, the *American Anthropologist* bore little resemblance to its predecessor.

Another difference had to do with economics. The Smithsonian Institution had underwritten the *Transactions*, but responsibility for the *American Anthropologist* was entirely in the hands of the Society—a burden which proved heavier than had been originally bargained for. At the outset it was felt that the new journal could be financed solely by subscriptions, selling for three dollars, allowing those who paid the annual membership fee to receive the *American Anthropologist* for no additional charge. This was wishful thinking. Early subscribers were few, and it became immediately clear that if a second volume was ever to see the light of day it would be necessary to raise the cost for members. Accordingly dues went up to five dollars a year. This enabled the *American Anthropologist* to carry on and, under the circumstances, was justifiable as a temporary measure. But what began as a makeshift arrangement came to be accepted as the *modus operandi*, and instead of forthrightly addressing itself to the problem of insufficient subscriptions the Society continued to operate at a loss by printing journals that it did not sell. In this respect the members supplied evidence for John Dewey's assertion that we do not solve old questions, we get over them.[62] Except that before the problem of paying for the *American Anthropologist* could be gotten over matters suddenly took a turn for the worse, making it imperative that some means for enlarging subscriptions be devised.

The middle 1890's were marked by panic and depression throughout the United States, and while the national economy stumbled the Society fell on hard times. The *American Anthropologist* had been such a financial drain that the Society now found itself faced with insolvency. A further increase of membership dues was out of the question; this left only the alternative of boosting subscriptions. Late in 1895, as President Cleveland desperately sought to rescue the government from bankruptcy, the Board of Managers hit upon a plan that would stave off economic disaster.

During its brief existence the Anthropological Society of Washington had accumulated a large stockpile of unsold publications. There is no record of members becoming upset about this. Instead they duplicated the sardonic resignation of a fellow naturalist who had suffered similarly at the hands of public indifference: "I now have a library of nearly nine hundred volumes," noted Henry David Thoreau in 1851, "over seven hundred of which I wrote myself. Is it not well that the author should behold the fruits of his labor?"[63] During the lean years of the nineties cold comfort could be taken from such luxuries—especially since the Society had over two thousand dollars worth of back numbers gathering dust. It was decided to sort these into eight volume sets and offer them to likely institutions at the regular price of three dollars per volume. In this way schools and libraries purchasing new subscriptions could receive complete series of the *American Anthropologist,* and the society would turn an otherwise useless collection of old issues into a source of badly needed revenue.[64]

Beginning in autumn 1895 almost four hundred letters were mailed to potential subscribers throughout the country, inviting them to purchase "one of the few remaining complete sets" of the *American Anthropologist.* The initial response was gratifying. Within a few weeks eight sets were disposed of bringing the Society almost two hundred dollars. By the end of 1896 five more had been sold and the situation seemed no longer critical. Coincident with this sales campaign were alterations made in the price and publication schedule. Starting with Volume IX annual subscriptions were reduced to two dollars and the number of issues increased to twelve. Thus the *American Anthropologist* was converted from a quarterly into a monthly magazine, a change designed to give it wider popular appeal.[65]

The drive to add buyers resulted in a period of fleeting success. Immediately subscriptions shot up by twenty-five per cent, but at the lower price this was not enough to place the Society on a firm footing. Indeed operating the monthly turned out to be more expensive than the quarterly. Within a matter of months the treasury showed a credit of only $7.28, and future prospects were so grim that consideration was given to selling the Society's library. A better course of action was to look outside the Society for financial aid.[66]

Fortunately, the American Association for the Advancement of Science had been sufficiently impressed with the journal to assume a large share of responsibility for keeping it alive. On June 14, 1898, at the Cosmos Club, representatives of the AAAS met with the Society's officers and agreed to assist with the management of the *American Anthropologist* as well as help pay the bills. Before this backing was secured, however, the Board of Managers outlined certain changes that promised to make the journal more useful to professionals. The January, 1899 number would begin a new series of quarterly issues. Obviously the magazine format had missed the mark, and it was roundly agreed that working anthropologists needed a scholarly journal. It was even suggested that the publication be called the *Journal of Anthropology,* but this was discarded in favor of the traditional title. Also, both the size and the price of a volume would be doubled, to eight hundred pages and four dollars respectively.[67]

Of greatest importance was the fact that the sponsoring agency was now the Anthropology Section of the AAAS. The *American Anthropologist* would continue to speak for the Washington organization— that was made emphatically clear— but as the organ for and not of the Society. New York rather than Washington served as the seat of publication, with overseas editions published in London and Leipzig. For the first time the editorial board included men who were not Society members, and no more was the Society's name and crest emblazoned on the journal's cover. Thus, the guiding hand of the Society had been removed from the *American Anthropologist.*

In a larger sense, however, the new series signaled a brilliant success for the Anthropological Society of Washington. Its original purpose was to promote anthropology and diffuse knowledge about the subject; now there existed a means to achieve that objective, and to the Society went the credit for its creation. Without the Society there would have been no journal. Therefore the members could indulge in a little self-congratulation over the new *American Anthropologist*. It was far and away the pre-eminent vehicle of anthropological information in the western hemisphere, and also had a regular distribution in England and Europe. Its articles covered all branches of anthropology and its influence transcended local and even national boundaries.

Furthermore, its editors were leading lights in the emerging profession, and their institutional ties effectively linked various centers of professional activity. Daniel Brinton represented the University of Pennsylvania; Franz Boas the American Museum of Natural History; George A. Dorsey the Field Columbian Museum. Frederick Ward Putnam was both president of the AAAS and curator of Harvard's Museum of American Archaeology and Ethnology. Then there were Hodge, Holmes, and Powell from the Smithsonian's Bureau of Ethnology. So an immediate result of the new series was to mesh more closely the network of professional interconnections joining the university and the federal government, and covering Philadelphia, New York, Chicago, Cambridge, and Washington. Here was what the Washington group had desired all along, an achievement which reflected the Society's maturity as an agent for the promotion of anthropology.

By any reckoning the Anthropological Society of Washington was no longer a fledgling organization. Just as early trepidation in the matter of publishing a journal bespoke weakness, so founding the *American Anthropologist* denoted strength. As early as 1888 all doubts had been erased as to whether the Society would survive. With its permanent home at the Cosmos Club, and after its incorporation in 1887 for a term of one thousand years, the Society exuded robust self-confidence.

In less than a decade, what began as an experiment involving fewer than thirty Washingtonians had surpassed the greatest expectations of its founders. Frank Hamilton Cushing was pleasantly surprised, in 1879, when the Society showed sufficient progress to warrant another year's activity.[68] Its growth continued, however, and at the time of incorporation there were 265 members. Paralleling this steady rise in membership was an expansion of the Society's orbit so that it became increasingly national and even international in scope. *Science* magazine carried reports of its proceedings, thereby bringing the Society to the attention of men outside Washington and helping to attract members the world over. In 1888 there were 115 members from places other than Washington, including thirty-seven from abroad. A few years later W J McGee, promoter and booster of Washington's scientific community, epitomized the spirit of the Society:

> The Anthropological Society of Washington was instituted in 1879 and for some years drifted easily with the tide; but of late it has awakened into activity, its membership has reached about 350, and its meetings have come to be largely attended, to the extent that many anthropologists hold these meetings to afford the best means in the country of making public the results of their work. . . .[69]

McGee's ardor was well founded, for through its deeds the Society had proclaimed its importance to the advancement of anthropology.

Most obvious were its unstinting efforts to drum up popular enthusiasm for this branch of science. Neither energy nor expense were spared in carrying out this aim, and no opportunity was neglected for swelling the ranks of anthropology's devotees. Thus, in the summer of 1885, when feminism asserted itself in anthropological circles, little time was lost helping to organize the Women's Anthropological Society of America.

Apart from receiving periodic aid, however, the Women's Society had a character all its own which derived from the achievements of its key members. Certainly the most famous was Alice Cunningham Fletcher, who became something of a living legend. Known as "Her Majesty," because of her short, Victoria-like figure, she was an assistant to Putnam at the Peabody, a collaborator of the Bureau of Ethnology, an editor of the *American Anthropologist,* and a founder and vice-president of the Women's Anthropolgical Society of America. Beginning in the early eighties her summers were spent in Nebraska among the Omahas. She was fired with a humanitarian zeal to erase ethnological ignorance, to save the Omahas and Sioux "from the grasping 'agency whites,' " and she spoke proudly of how she "left her scientific studies to pester the congressmen and senators to *do* something for the Indians."[70]

The new group's most inimitable personality and driving force was its founder and first president, Matilda Coxe Stevenson. As an ethnologist, Tilly Stevenson spent nearly a decade hidden in the official shadow of her husband James. While he held the responsible position of executive officer of the Bureau of Ethnology, she plodded dutifully behind as his unheralded colleague. But her consciousness had been raised, and when given the opportunity she urged her sisters not to be timid about stepping forward and assuming their rightful place in the profession— which to Mrs. Stevenson meant the front rank that was denied her for so long. In 1888, after James Stevenson's death, she was appointed to the Bureau's staff, and eleven years later gained further satisfaction from the integration of the Anthropological Society of Washington, thus symbolizing "the general, unqualified acceptance of women in anthropology."[71]

Anita Newcomb McGee was only twenty-four when the Women's Society elected her its recording secretary. Even at that early stage of her career she commanded respect, initially as the daughter of Simon Newcomb, then as the wife of W J, but ultimately because of her individual merits. Self-confident, intellectually nimble, and full of vitality, she obtained an M.D. degree (with postgraduate specialization in gynecology) while raising her family. During the Spanish-American War she organized and won congressional approval of the Army Nurse Corps, securing for herself an appointment as acting assistant surgeon, United States Army. Clearly, Dr. McGee had an unerring sense of the role women might play in late nineteenth century science.[72]

The Women's Anthropological Society of America was no mere ladies auxiliary. Justifying its existence according to "the intellectual future that is opening to all women," it held that women were specially qualified to make discoveries that would forever elude men and otherwise be lost to human understanding. As mothers they were more sensitive to "the earliest unfoldings of thought, language, and belief;" as teachers and physicians they had a unique opportunity to record the practices of child nuture and the habits of the young; and simply as women they could better comprehend relationships between the sexes in comparative cultures. Home and hearth thereby enhanced insights and natural apptitudes, while the participation of women in an intellectual enterprise gave a higher meaning to domesticity. The new Society believed that women could make singular contributions without forsaking their current occupations. Its statement of purpose stressed that "The new fields that open before us are not those requiring new occupation, but, rather, new observation. Women are not exhorted to *leave* present life-conditions, but to *master* them in the interest of science."[73]

Standing also for an equal place for the professional woman, it coveted independence and only obliquely acknowledged its debt to the Anthropological Society of Washington. Yet there were enough similarities between them to indicate that the former was patterned after the men's organization. In purpose they were identical and in polity almost so. Like the

Anthropological Society, the Women's Society was divided into specialized sections (archeology, child-life, ethnology, folklore, psychology, and
sociology); meetings were held biweekly, November through April, and
consisted of lectures and discussions; records of proceedings were published annually; membership requirements were negligible; and governance was centralized in a Board of Directors. The Women's Society also
followed the example of forging ahead with its operations even though few
of its members were trained professionals (in 1885 only Tilly Stevenson
had done scientific work), and of being cautious about starting publications during its early life.

Why then was it necessary to have two separate organizations? Anita
McGee answered the question:

> Speaking for ourselves, we have no desire to perpetuate a distinction of
> sex in science; and were we all professional scientists or possessed of educa-
> tion fitting us to enter the race for intellectual attainment without handicap,
> we doubt whether a second society would ever have been formed. Under
> existing conditions, however, we are satisfied to work out our own problems
> in anticipation of the time when science shall regard only the work, not the
> worker.

Here was a direct response to second class status, to the aggravations of
being encouraged to participate in anthropology, but only in a subordinate
capacity. By not mincing words, Dr. McGee further expressed a fierce
pride in the fact that of all the scientific societies in the United States, "the
first to be organized and maintained by women alone is the Women's
Anthropological Society of America."[74]

This campaign for women's rights in science won some tokens of assistance from the Society. In 1889 the creation of a library was helped by
Major Powell, who offered the women shelf space which he had reserved
for their use at the Bureau of Ethnology. On several occasions in the nineties the Anthropological Society arranged for the Societies to meet jointly.
Usually this was for the purpose of hearing a visiting lecturer, and when
the guest was a female, the Women's Anthropological Society of America
served as the host organization. Cooperation of this sort was facilitated by
the fact that certain leaders in both Societies were husband and wife, notably the Weston Flints, the Masons, the McGees, and the Stevensons. Thus
the Anthropological Society of Washington had something of a vested
interest in the Women's Anthropological Society of America. By contrib-

uting to its success the Society was simultaneously aiding the cause of anthropology.[75]

The Society also promoted the study of man through public lectures held at the National Museum. Inaugurated in March, 1882, the Saturday Lectures were intended to introduce audiences of non-specialists to recent discoveries and advances. Otis T. Mason's "What is Anthropology?" might be taken as an archetypical attempt to give the intelligent layman a better understanding of this particular branch of science. Mason also exemplified the quality of lecturers, who invariably were men of recognized competence. William Henry Holmes, Mallery, McGee, Powell, and other familiar figures perennially donated their services, thereby reaffirming their commitments to the popularization of scientific knowledge. It was through their efforts that the Saturday Lectures came to be a permanent fixture of Washington's intellectual life. Except for a temporary lapse in the early nineties, every year saw a series of at least twelve lectures which were structured into three or four weekly courses, each having a definite theme. By this approach residents of the Federal City were able to experience a little of the excitement that colored late nineteenth century science in America.

All through the 1880's the Society persistently sought to arouse interest in scientific pursuits, but nothing matched its bid for popular attention in 1893. At the annual meeting that year an amendment to the by-laws was passed which permitted the Board of Managers to "offer prizes for notable original contributions to anthropology." This was the work of W J McGee whose ambitious schemes for himself and the Society sometimes raised the hackles of fellow Board members.[76] In 1892 he had tried to change the by-laws so that income from life memberships would be earmarked for monetary prizes. The gathering clouds of depression, plus the Society's shaky economic status, made this seem unwise, and McGee's proposal was not accepted by the Board. But shortly thereafter the Society voted unanimously in favor of bestowing awards provided the funds came from another source. Now McGee had all the leeway he needed, for his powers of solicitation were great. In no time he secured a benefactor from the ranks of the Society, Dr. Robert H. Lamborn of New York, who also belonged to the Anthropology Section of the AAAS and was a firm believer in the popularization of scientific knowledge.[77] At the end of March came the announcement that the Anthropological Society of Washington was offering awards of one hundred twenty-five dollars and seventy-five dollars for the two "clearest statements of the elements that go to make up the most useful citizen regardless of occupation," a topic blending current concerns over social tensions and the Society's inclusiveness. Other than a maximum limit of two thousand words and a stipulation that essays bear pseudonyms, there were no rules for contestants to follow. The citizenship essay competition was underway.[78]

From many parts of the United States, as well as from Denmark, England, Spain, Syria, and Java compositions poured in to McGee who was chairman of the Prize Committee. After forty-two manuscripts had been received, the competition was closed and the business of evaluation commenced. First a preliminary screening of all papers was performed by McGee's committee which included Cushing, Flint, and Mason. Papers entirely devoid of merit were eliminated, while the twenty-five or thirty that survived were given provisional grades. Then the essays went to a panel of final judges consisting of Daniel Brinton, Melville W. Fuller, Chief Justice of the United States, Daniel Coit Gilman, Vice-President Adlai E. Stevenson, and Dr. Lamborn. These Commissioners of Award had been painstakingly selected by McGee who operated on the premise that admirable, well established Americans were best able to judge qualities of ideal citizenship.[79]

Their verdict considered strength of individual character and loyalty to republican institutions to be the requisite virtues. This was predictable considering the patriotic impulse which American culture produced in the 1890's as an antidote to radicalism.[80] Totally unexpected, however, was the awarding of the second prize to the chairman of the Prize Committee, his essay being deemed superior to all others except that written by his father-in-law, Simon Newcomb. McGee confessed privately that he had submitted the paper hoping that this would prompt other members of the Society to enter manuscripts. Ironically, his attempt to generate enthusiasm turned into a source of embarrassment and regret when the awards were announced.[81] After the winning essays appeared in the October, 1894 *American Anthropologist,* expressions of dissatisfaction followed from unsuccessful authors. Both the administration of the contest and the standards of judgement were taken to task, along lines similar to a letter from Parkman, Ohio which concluded: "Now if your Society together with Mr. Newcomb and the commission of eminent men will come to this town [and] attend the public school you may learn that which you ought to have learned before by studying some reading lessons in Appleton's Fifth Reader . . . ."[82]

Actually the essay competition could not have been more in keeping with the aims and character of the Anthropological Society of Washington. "The elements that go to make up the most useful citizen" was a subject as broad as Mason's definition of anthropology, and conformed to the *American Anthropologist's* principle of encouraging articles "not burdened with technicalities."[83] Notices of the competition had been printed in learned journals as well as newspapers with general readerships. Thus the Society remained true to its policy of serving at once specialists and laymen. Yet while the essay contest was open to all—just as the invitation to participate in the Society was freely extended—it was subtly dominated by a handful of professionals. In other words, the subsurface condition of elitist direction which prevailed in the Society was perpetuated in the competition. Finally, the citizenship essay contest was designed to provide national publicity and to encourage the study of anthropology in its widest sense.

These factors were very much on the mind of W J McGee, who never permitted his thoughts to wander far from considerations of the prestige and promotion of Washington's intellectual community. His fertile brain conceived of a galaxy of learned bodies at the Capital, aiding the advancement of science and culture while developing concurrently with the disciplines they sustained. This mental image encapsulated the early history of the Anthropological Society of Washington. Especially important was its seminal influence in the creation of intellectual organizations during the late nineteenth century. It was, to borrow the organic metaphor that his wife used in relation to her Society, "the minute seed from which a great forest will spring."[84]

NOTES TO CHAPTER 5

1. *The Evening Star* (Washington, D. C.), February 7, 1879, p. 1.

2. For descriptions of Mallery by contemporaries see Robert Fletcher, *Brief Memoirs of Colonel Garrick Mallery, U.S.A., Who Died October 24, 1894* (Washington, D. C., 1895); John Wesley Powell, "Garrick Mallery," *Johnson's Universal Cyclopaedia*, V, ed. Charles Kendall Adams, (1897) 496; *Annual Report of the Board of Regents of the Smithsonian Institution for the Year Ending June 30, 1895* (Washington, D. C., 1896), pp. 52-53.

3. Garrick Mallery to Capt. Richard H. Pratt, October 29, 1879, Letters Sent, Box 1, Correspondence of the Bureau of American Ethnology, National Anthropological Archives, Smithsonian Institution (henceforth BAE, SI).

4. Richard H. Pratt to Frank H. Cushing, December 27, 1881, Cushing Papers, Southwest Museum Library.

5. Richard Henry Pratt, *Battlefield and Classroom: Four Decades With the American Indian, 1867-1904*, ed. Robert M. Utley (New Haven, Conn., 1964), p. 293.

6. Thomas Jefferson, *Notes On the State of Virginia*, ed. William Peden (Chapel Hill, N. C., 1954), p. 101.

7. Don D. Fowler and Catherine S. Fowler, "John Wesley Powell, Anthropologist," *Utah Historical Quarterly*, XXXVII (Spring, 1969), 154-158; for an interesting discussion of the influence of the "vanishing savage" concept on anthropological method, see Jacob W. Gruber, "Ethnographic Salvage and the Shaping of Anthropology," *American Anthropologist*, LXXII (December, 1970), 1289-1299.

8. J. W. Powell, *Report on the Methods of Surveying the Public Domain, to the Secretary of the Interior, at the Request of the National Academy of Sciences* (Washington, D. C., 1878), p. 16.

9. Garrick Mallery, "The Former and Present Number of Our Indians," *Proceedings of the American Association for the Advancement of Science*, XXVI (1878), 366 (henceforth AAAS *Proceedings*).

10. John G. Bourke to Frank H. Cushing, December 5, 1894, Cushing Papers, Southwest Museum Library.

11. Otis T. Mason to William J. Rhees, January 11, 1904, Rhees Collection, RH 3566, Box 55, Henry E. Huntington Library and Art Gallery.

12. "Otis T. Mason," *The Popular Science Monthly,* LXXIV (January, 1909), 98; Journal of Joseph Henry, January 10, 1875, Henry Papers, Smithsonian Institution Archives; *Report of the United States National Museum, 1884* (Washington, D. C., 1885), pp. 56-57.

13. Ernest Ingersoll, "The Making of a Museum," *The Century Magazine,* XXIX (January, 1885), 356-357; G. Brown Goode, *Museum-History and Museums of History* (New York, 1889), pp. 263-265; Goode, who as assistant secretary of the Smithsonian was in charge of the Museum, later specified three classes of people for whom the collections had to be made interesting: professionals doing research, college students, and casual visitors, *Report of the U. S. National Museum, 1891* (Washington, D. C., 1892), pp. 5-6.

14. For the Mason years at Woodlawn see, Tony P. Wrenn, "After the Lewises: Life at Woodlawn 1846-1972," *Historic Preservation,* XXIV (October-December, 1972), 26-31.

15. Otis T. Mason, "What is Anthropology?" *The Saturday Lectures . . . 1882* (Washington, D. C., 1882), pp. 26-27; Jesse Walter Fewkes, "Anthropology," *The Smithsonian Institution 1846-1896: The History of Its First Half Century,* ed. George Brown Goode (Washington, D. C., 1897), p. 768.

16. Ales Hrdlicka, "Otis Tufton Mason," *Science,* N. S., XXVIII (November 27, 1908), 747.

17. Ainsworth R. Spofford, "Memorial of Dr. Joseph M. Toner," *Annual Report of the Board of Regents of the the Smithsonian Institution for the Year Ending June 30, 1896* (Washington, D. C., 1898), p. 638.

18. *Ibid.,* p. 640.

19. Thomas Neville Bonner, *Medicine in Chicago, 1850-1950: A Chapter in the Social and Scientific Development of a City* (Madison, Wisc., 1957), pp. 82-83; Thomas Antisell, *Biographical Sketch of Joseph M. Toner, M.D., of Washington* (Lancaster, Pa., 1878), p. 16.

20. Minutes of the first preliminary meeting, February 10, 1879, Records of the

Anthropological Society of Washington, MSS Collection 4821, Box 2, National Anthropological Archives, Smithsonian Institution (henceforth ASW Records, SI); a list of those who attended the February 10 meeting is contained in Daniel S. Lamb, "The Story of the Anthropological Society of Washington," *American Anthropologist*, N. S., VII (July-September, 1906), 565; a slightly different list was printed in *The Evening Star* (Washington, D. C.), February 11, 1879, p. 4

21. *Annual Report [1879] of the National Academy of Sciences* (Washington, D. C., 1880), pp. 20-22.

22. AAAS *Proceedings*, XXVIII (1880), vi, x, xxviii-liv.

23. *Boyd's Directory of the District of Columbia* [1879] . . . comp. Wm. H. Boyd (Washington, D. C., 1878), *passim*.

24. U. S. Bureau of the Census, *Tenth Census of the United States: 1880. District of Columbia*, I, 46, U. S. National Archives microfilm.

25. Geoffrey Millerson, *The Qualifying Associations: A Study in Professionalization* (London, 1964), p. 12; George H. Daniels, "The Process of Professionalization in American Science: The Emergent Period, 1820-1860," *Isis*, (LVIII (Summer, 1967), 156.

26. *The Evening Star* (Washington, D. C.), February 11, 1879, p. 4.

27. A.M. Carr-Saunders and P. A. Wilson, *The Professions* (Oxford, 1933), p. 295.

28. Pertinent to the origins and implications of academic professionalization are, Regna Diebold Darnell, "The Development of American Anthropology 1879-1920: From the Bureau of American Ethnology to Franz Boas" (unpublished Ph.D. dissertation, Department of Anthropology, University of Pennsylvania, 1969), pp. 140-166; Hamilton Cravens, "The Abandonment of Evolutionary Social Theory in America: The Impact of Academic Professionalization Upon American Sociological Theory, 1890-1920," *American Studies*, XII (Fall, 1971), 6-10; Mary O. Furner, "Advocacy and Objectivity: The Professionalization of Social Science 1865-1905" (unpublished Ph.D. dissertation, Department of History, Northwestern University, June, 1972), pp. 1-6; John D. Holmfeld, "From Amateurs to Professionals in American Science: The Controversy Over the Proceedings of an 1853 Scientific Meeting," *Proceedings of the American Philosophical Society*, CIV (February 16, 1970), 36 (henceforth APS Proceedings); Daniels, *Isis*, LVIII, 152-156; see also his *American Science in the Age of Jackson* (New York, 1968), pp. 34-40; Howard S. Miller, *Dollars for Research:*

Science and Its Patrons in Nineteenth-Century America (Seattle, Wash., 1970), pp. 71-99, 151-165; Barry D. Karl, "The Power of Intellect and the Politics of Ideas," *Daedalus*, XC (Summer, 1968), 1002-1035; Stanley Coben, "The Scientific Establishment and the Transmission of Quantum Mechanics to the United States, 1919-32," *American Historical Review*, LXX (April, 1971), 442-466.

29. Lamb, *American Anthropologist*, N. S., VIII, 566.

30. Fowler and Fowler, *Utah Historical Quarterly*, XXXVII, 169; Darnell, "Development of American Anthropology," p. 4; see also, Roy Harvey Pearce, *The Savages of America: A Study of the Indian and the Idea of Civilization*, rev. ed. (Baltimore, Md., 1965), p. 130.

31. "Report of Joseph Henry, Secretary, for the Year 1877," *Annual Report of the Board of Regents of the Smithsonian Institution . . . for the Year 1877* (Washington, D. C., 1878), p. 22.

32. Miller, *Dollars for Research*, p. 143.

33. J. W. Powell to S. F. Baird, October 23, 1880, MSS Collection 4677, Bureau History, clerk's correspondence between S. F. Baird and Frank H. Cushing and John Wesley Powell, BAE, SI.

34. *Ibid.*, July 2, 1880, January 17, 1882, August 21, 1882, June 27, 1883, and August 4, 1883; "No personnel or salary list is known for this period," Neil P. Judd, *The Bureau of American Ethnology: A Partial History* (Norman, Okla., 1967), p. 11.

35. On the importance of the public's desire to share "in the inner mysteries of the profession" see, Daniels, *American Science in the Age of Jackson*, p. 41, and *Isis*, LVIII, 160-166; a contemporary view is presented in, Ellen Hardin Walworth, "Field Work by Amateurs," AAAS *Proceedings*, XXIX (1880), 597-602.

36. Mason, *Saturday Lectures . . . 1882*, p. 26.

37. Otis T. Mason to Franz Boas, December 3, 1887, Boas Papers, American Philosophical Society; Otis T. Mason, "Anthropology in the District of Columbia: Its Present Status and Its History," p. 31, paper prepared for the Anthropological Society of Washington and read by Walter Hough, April 10, 1906, Box 4, ASW Records, SI.

38. Verne F. Ray and Nancy Oestreich Lurie, "The Contributions of Lewis and

Clark to Ethnology," *Journal of the Washington Academy of Sciences,* XLIV (November, 1954), 358, 361.

39. J. W. Powell, "Sketch of Lewis H. Morgan, President of the American Association for the Advancement of Science," *The Popular Science Monthly,* XVIII (November, 1880), 121; on Powell's indebtedness to Morgan see, Fowler and Fowler, *Utah Historical Quarterly,* XXXVII, 153.

40. W. H. Holmes, "Biographical Memoir of Lewis Henry Morgan, 1818-1881," *National Academy of Sciences Biographical Memoirs,* VI (1909), 221.

41. Jacob W. Gruber, "Horatio Hale and the Development of American Anthropology," APS *Proceedings,* CXI (February 17, 1967), 6.

42. Carl Resek, *Lewis Henry Morgan: American Scholar* (Chicago, 1960), pp. 27-40; Bernhard J. Stern, *Lewis Henry Morgan: Social Evolutionist* (Chicago, 1931), pp. 16-19.

43. Panchanan Mitra, *A History of American Anthropology* (Calcutta, India, 1933), p. 120; for a recent appraisal of Morgan, an account of the cycles through which his reputation has passed, and a perceptive analysis of his pivotal role in nineteenth century anthropology, see Robert Eugene Bieder, "The American Indian and the Development of Anthropological Thought in the United States, 1780-1851" (unpublished Ph.D. dissertation, Department of History, University of Minnesota, August, 1972), pp. 367-410.

44. Thomas S. Kuhn, *The Structure of Scientific Revolutions,* 2d ed., enl. (Chicago, 1970), pp. 18-19; Nathan Reingold has kindly made available to me his fresh interpretation of this problem, in unpublished form, "Definitions and Speculations: The Professionalization of Science in America in the Nineteenth Century" (1973), prepared for the American Academy of Arts and Sciences' Conference on the History of Learned Societies in America; pertinent also is his, "National Aspirations and Local Purposes," *Transactions of the Kansas Academy of Science,* LXXI (Fall, 1968), 235-246.

45. Kuhn, *Structure of Scientific Revolutions,* pp. 10-11, 15-19.

46. Robert V. Bruce, "A Statistical Profile of American Scientists, 1846-1876," *Nineteenth Century American Science: A Reappraisal,* ed. George H. Daniels (Evanston, Ill., 1972), p. 68.

47. Henry Carrington Bolton (ed.), *A Catalogue of Scientific and Technical Periodicals, 1665-1895* . . . 2d ed. (Washington, D. C., 1897), p. 804; Donald deB. Beaver, "The American Scientific Community, 1800-1860: A Statistical-Historical

Study" (unpublished Ph.D. dissertation, Department of History of Science and Medicine, Yale University, 1966), p. 257.

48. Darnell, "Development of American Anthropology," pp. 148-154; in England, "it was not until 1896 that Oxford fully recognized the new science, established a professorship of anthropology, and gave it to [Edward] Tylor," Morse Peckham, *Victorian Revolutionaries: Speculations on Some Heroes of a Culture Crisis* (New York, 1970), p. 176.

49. Daniels, *Isis,* LVIII, 154, and his "The Pure-Science Ideal and Democratic Culture," *Science, CLVI* (June, 1967), 1701, and *American Science in the Age of Jackson* pp. 38-39; Furner, "Advocacy and Objectivity," p. 2; William G. Rothstein, *American Physicians in the Nineteenth Century: From Sects to Science* (Baltimore, Md., 1972), p. 8.

50. The enormous popular interest in anthropology, ethnology, archaeology, and antiquities is borne out by, Answers to Circular, file box labeled Names of People Baird Knew, Baird Papers, SI Archives; A. Irving Hallowell, "The Beginnings of Anthropology in America," *Selected Papers From the American Anthropologist, 1888-1920,* ed. Frederica De Laguna (Evanston, Ill., 1960), p. 37; Franz Boas, "The History of Anthropology," *Science,* N. S., XX (October 21, 1904), 513, 522.

51. Frank H. Cushing to Otis T. Mason, September 30, 1876, Cushing Papers, Southwest Museum Library.

52. Quoted in Miller, *Dollars for Research,* p. 7.

53. I am indebted to Hamilton Cravens for his insights as presented in "Professionalization and the Origins of the Culture Concept in the American Social Sciences, 1890-1940" (November, 1972), prepared for the Southern Historical Association, pp. 2-9; see also his "Abandonment of Sociological Theory," *American Studies,* XII, 6-9.

54. The importance of "Self-Definition" as a transitional phase of professionalization is explained in Sally Kohlstedt, "A Step Toward Scientific Self-Identity in the United States: The Failure of the National Institute, 1844," *Isis,* LXII (September, 1971), 339-362; for a stimulating discussion of the tension between the "two types of professionalism" represented by the preacademic Washingtonians and the Boasians, see George W. Stocking, Jr., "The Scientific Reaction Against Cultural Anthropology, 1917-1920," *Race, Culture, and Evolution: Essays in the History of Anthropology* (New York, 1968), pp. 277-284.

55. Minutes of the second preliminary meeting, February 17, 1879, Box 2, ASW Records, SI.

56. W J McGee to Otis T. Mason, May 25, 1893, Correspondence, letterpress volume labeled, "Letters Sent to Speakers, March 5, 1892-October, 1895," Box 8, *Ibid.*; G. K. Gilbert to Marcus Benjamin, July 24, 1888, Box 5, Benjamin Papers, Smithsonian Institution Archives; *Transactions of the Anthropological Society of Washington*, I-III (Washington, D. C., 1882-1885), *passim*.

57. Lamb, *American Anthropologist*, N. S., VIII, 568-569; Frank Baker, Annual Report of the General Secretary for 1891, Minutes of the Meeting of January 19, 1892, Box 3, ASW Records, SI.

58. Minutes of the Board of Managers, *passim*, Box 5, *ibid.*

59. Speakers were almost always active members, though on occasion a special lecturer such as Franz Boas, Alfred R. Wallace, Mrs. Zelia Nuttal from Berlin, or E. B. Tylor, the English anthropologist who was an honorary member of the Society, would read an address.

60. W J McGee to H Ioracel E. Warner, January 7, 1893, Correspondence, letterpress volume labeled, "Letters Sent to Speakers, March 5, 1892-October, 1895," Box 8, ASW Records, SI.

61. G. Brown Goode, *The Beginnings of American Science, the Third Century* (Washington, D. C., 1888), pp. 91-92.

62. John Dewey, "The Influence of Darwinism on Philosophy," *American Thought: Civil War to World War I*, ed. Perry Miller (New York, 1954; Rinehart edn., New York, 1962), p. 224.

63. Henry David Thoreau, *A Week On the Concord and Merrimack Rivers* (Boston, 1849; Sentry edn., Cambridge, Mass., 1961), p. xl.

64. Frederick W. Hodge, Report of the Curator for 1895, January 21, 1896, Curator's Reports 1891-1897, Box 12, ASW Records, SI.

65. F. W. Hodge to the Librarian, Keokuk Iowa Library Association, January 16, 1896, Correspondence, letterpress volume labeled, "Letters Sent Concerning the Publication and Distribution of the American Anthropologist, Dec. 31, 1892-Feb. 3, 1896," Box 8; Frederick W. Hodge, Report of the Curator for 1895, Curator's Reports 1891-1897, Box 12; Minutes of the Board of Managers, December 15, 1896, Box 5, *ibid.*

66. Frederick W. Hodge, Report of the Curator for 1895, Curator's Reports 1891-1897, Box 12, ASW Records, SI; Cyrus Adler to W J McGee, November 20, 1897, and Perry B. Pierce to W J McGee, November 30, 1897, McGee Papers, General Correspondence, Box 1, Manuscript Division, Library of Congress.

67. Minutes of the Board of Managers, March 15, 1898 and November 1, 1898, Box 5, ASW Records, SI.

68. Frank H. Cushing to [?] Turner, May 15, 1879, Cushing Papers, Southwest Museum Library.

69. W J McGee to Prof. Francis A. March, October 31, 1892, Correspondence, letterpress volume labeled, "Letters Sent to Speakers, March 5, 1892-October, 1895," Box 8, ASW Records, SI.

70. Jane Gay Dodge, "Sketch of My First Meeting With Alice C. Fletcher in 1888" (1939), folder 1, Dodge Papers, The Arthur and Elizabeth Schlesinger Library on the History of Women in America, Radcliffe College; Thurman Wilkins, "Alice Cunningham Fletcher," *Notable American Women 1607-1950: A Biographical Dictionary*, eds. Edward T. James, Janet Wilson James, and Paul S. Boyer (Cambridge, Mass., 1971), I, 630-633.

71. Nancy Ostreich Lurie, "Matilda Coxe Evans Stevenson," *ibid.*, III, 373-374; Mrs. Stevenson was the terror of the Bureau: "She is described as a strong-willed and dominating individual; she commanded others to do her bidding. What she wanted she took — even a chair someone else might be using," Judd, *Bureau of American Ethnology*, p. 57; for an excellent account of her, Miss Fletcher, and the Women's Anthropological Society of America, see Nancy Ostreich Lurie, "Women in Early Anthropology," *Pioneers of American Anthropology: The Uses of Biography*, ed. June Helm (Seattle, Wash., 1966), 31-81.

72. Mary R. Dearing, "Anita Newcomb McGee," *Notable American Women*, II, 464-466; "Anita Newcomb McGee," *The National Cyclopaedia of American Biography* ... (New York, 1909), X, 350.

73. *The Organization and the Constitution of the Women's Anthropological Society* (Washington, D. C. [1885]), pp. 11, 9.

74. Anita Newcomb McGee, "Historical Sketch of the Women's Anthropological Society of America," *Organization and Historical Sketch of the Women's Anthropological Society of America* (Washington, D. C., 1889), 16-17, 22; see also, *Science*, XIII (March 29, 1889), 240-241; a fascinating testament to their concern with feminism is, A Innie] Tolman Smith, "Genetic Development of the

Woman's [sic] Anthropological Society, *Proceedings of the One Hundredth Meeting, January 28, 1893* (Washington, D. C., 1893), pp. 9-31; women in early anthropology were not discriminated against so much as they were treated condescendingly by their male counterparts, Lurie, "Women," *Pioneers of American Anthropology*, 32-33, 40-41.

75. W J McGee to Mrs. Susan A. Mendenhall, November 24, 1893, W J McGee to Colonel Weston Flint, March 8, 1894, and W J McGee to Dr. Washington Matthews, March 23, 1895, Correspondence, letterpress volume labeled, "Letters Sent to Speakers, March 5, 1892-October, 1895," Box 8, ASW Records, SI.

76. O. T. Mason to F.W. Hodge, January 11, 1893, folder labeled, "Letters Received, 1890-99 M," Box 7; F. W. Hodge to O.T. Mason, January 14, 1893, Correspondence, letterpress volume labled, "Letters Sent Concerning the Publication and Distribution of the American Anthropologist," Dec. 31, 1892-Feb. 3, 1896, Box 8, ASW Records, SI.

77. Dr. Lamborn had appropriately been elected to the AAAS in 1879, AAAS *Proceedings*, XLII (1893), liv; Robert H. Lamborn to Lester F. Ward, December 24, 1890, Autographs, III, 50, Ward Papers, Brown University Library.

78. Minutes of the Anthropological Society of Washington, December 20, 1892 and January 17, 1893, Box 3, ASW Records, SI.

79. W J McGee to Daniel G. Brinton, March 5, 1894, and W J McGee to Robert H. Lamborn, March 26, 1894, Correspondence, letterpress volume labeled, "Letters Sent to Speakers, March 5, 1892-October, 1895," Box 8, *ibid.*

80. "None are anarchistic," reported McGee with an air of relief after he had examined the essays, W J McGee to Robert H. Lamborn, May 8, 1894, *ibid.;* on the upsurge of patriotism see, John Higham, "The Reorientation of American Culture in the 1890's," *The Origins of Modern Consciousness,* ed. John Weiss (Detoit, Mich., 1965), pp. 25-48.

81. W J McGee to Robert H. Lamborn, June 9, 1894, *ibid.*

82. W. J. Bestor to W J McGee, January 21, 1895, McGee Papers, General Correspondence, Box 1, Manuscript Division, Library of Congress.

83. Minutes of the Board of Managers, March 15, 1898, Box 5, ASW Records, SI.

84. Anita Newcomb McGee, "Historical Sketch," *Organization and Historical Sketch,* p. 22.

6

Within One Organization

The last two decades of the nineteenth century witnessed the creation of a series of homologous organizations which evolved into the Washington Academy of Sciences. First came the Biological Society in 1880, followed four years later by the Chemical and Entomological Societies, the National Geographic in 1888, and, in 1893, the Geological Society of Washington. This process rounded-out the formative phase of the Capital's intellectual community. By the end of the century there existed separate components for half a dozen scientific specialties, the Medical Society of the District of Columbia (which dated from 1817), and the recently established Columbia Historical Society, all fused into a local academy. Many new societies shared the same founders and officers, and frequently these men were also fellow members of the Cosmos Club. Thus the proliferation of independent bodies was accompanied by the strengthening of personal and institutional ties. Furthermore, the groups which emered in the eighties and nineties tended to hold mutual objectives and display similar characteristics. Each stood for the increase and diffusion of knowledge, a common aim which invariably led them to promote both professional research and popular interest. Strikingly, but not surprisingly—for they were rooted in the same soil as the Anthropological Society—they resembled branches of a single tree.

These societies began as outlets for men interested in particular fields of science. Usually, founders were employed by federal agencies and the establishment of societies reflected the maturity of their specialities in the government. The Geological was formed in the office of Charles D. Walcott, who would shortly succeed Powell as director of the United States Geological Survey; the Chemical was born at the Army Medical Museum; Charles V. Riley, of the Department of Agriculture, issued the call for the

Biological's first meeting. A dozen years later, when Riley defined its purpose as "the exchange of the experiences, discoveries, and opinions of the many different specialists who are doing original work connected with the Government," and concluded that "no other organization has done more during the time of its existence for American biology," he effectively summarized the valuable roles played by all Washington's societies in the eighties and nineties.[1]

New organizations did not result from influences that were entirely positive, however. To an extent their appearances were caused by the reluctance of the Philosophical Society to encourage special sections. When prospects for a geological body were under discussion, G. Bown Goode argued in favor of remaining within the older association, but to no avail. As the Biologists and Anthropoligists had already discovered, separation was the best way to achieve the desired combination of professional and amateur participation.[2]

In order to serve both experts and friends of science, membership in the societies was made easily attainable. For the most part only a majority vote was needed for admission and there were no special requirements for candidates. Indeed, constitutions were written so as to attract laymen. The Entomological, for example, welcomed those "in any way interested" in the study of entomology.[3] On the other hand, instruments of government guaranteed tight control by the executive councils. Invariably something resembling the skeletal structure of the Anthropological Society was adopted, and without exception this made for sturdy organization. While elections were held annually, certain men tended to be perennial office holders—and often in more than one group. The expedience of this practice is clear, though it is hard to imagine how some individuals were able to attend all the board meetings required of them.

Another feature borrowed from the Anthropological insured professional vigor: the division of members into specialized sections. The Biological Society made such a structuring one of its first items of business so that the presentation and discussion of technical papers would not be delayed.[4] This commitment of Washington's new scientific societies to professionalization was quickly acknowledged. In 1887, every American Chemical Society member in Washington resigned from the New York group and joined the local organization. This dramatic change of membership symbolized a shift in professional concentration and activity, while also testifying to the institution-building skills of government scientists. "Unlike the first [New York] effort to establish an independent national society, the second [Washington] was an unqualified success, due chiefly to the persistence, strategy, and tact of two Washington, D. C. professionals, Frank Clarke (then with the Geological Survey) and Harvey Wiley (of the Department of Agriculture). . . ." Clarke and Wiley would later revive the American Chemical Society, an achievement which followed from their having gained for the Chemical Society of Washington an influential role in the profession.[5]

Washington's professionals were the more gratified by the modest initiation and membership fees of their societies. Most organizations collected dues of only one or two dollars a year, the notable exception being the National Geographic Society which charged five dollars. Yet the National Geographic showed the greatest rise in membership, from 167 to 1,888 to almost 2,500 by the end of the century.[6]

Doubtless this was due to the quality of its journal, for while nearly all societies had publications, none was comparable to the *National Geographic Magazine*. Only the Geological Society failed to produce some sort of proceedings or bulletin of transactions prior to 1898. At the outset, as had been true of the *American Anthropologist*, these contained mere resumes and abstracts summarizing meetings, and despite the inevitable problems encountered in maintaining serials, they improved with age. It also became customary for journals to be distributed to libraries and research institutions on exchange bases. Thus, nineteen years after it first appeared, Lester Ward could legitimately state that the *Proceedings of the Biological Society of Washington* was as suitable a medium for original descriptions as any natural science journal in the country.[7] Nevertheless, it hardly surpassed the *Magazine* in either form or content.

The familiar *National Geographic* of today differs considerably from the late nineteenth century version which showed definite professional aspirations. In place of pictorial essays the original presented more scholarly papers, and rather than being primarily a popular culture periodical it served as a means of communication between geographers. "Its aim is to convey new information," wrote W J McGee in 1896, "and at the same time to reflect current opinion on geographic matters." "Diffusing interest" was also part of its purpose, [8] and the *Magazine* always had a wide appeal. By printing full length articles, the proceedings of the Society, correspondence and book reviews, and through the excellent maps which of course were a hallmark, the *Magazine* enjoyed immediate success. Much of its attraction could be credited to the brilliance of its editorial board. In the mid-nineties, the *Magazine* began reporting the arctic exploits of Lieutenant Robert E. Peary, a member of the Society. Other timely contributions dealt with the natural resources and geographical importance of the Caribbean Islands and the Philippines. The *National Geographic Magazine* was exceptional. Yet the publication with the reddish-brown cover (symbolically matching that of the Smithsonian buildings) seemed to stand for the vitality of Washington's intellectual community.

In addition to their publications, the societies used regular meetings for the transmission of scientific knowledge. With all groups having the same October through May schedule it was necessary to arrange dates so as to avoid conflicts for the many men belonging to more than one group. Also, the organizations shared common meeting sites: the Smithsonian before 1887, the Cosmos Club afterward, and the Builders' Exchange Hall which was used for annual meetings. January was when annual meetings customarily took place and on these occasions officers were elected and presidential addresses delivered. During the other months members and their guests heard and criticized technical papers. The Geological Society divided its time between "Informal Communications" and "Regular Programs," thereby providing for both extemporaneous remarks and lectures prepared in advance. Among all societies an average of roughly thirty to forty percent of the members came to meetings, with professionals comprising the core of every regular attendance. These were the men who gave and received the most from monthly sessions. As McGee said of the Geographers, "each contributes . . . to the common stock of knowledge . . . and their researches are stimulated by the encouragement and associations found in the Society."[9]

Promoting different branches of science also required whetting the public's appetite, and this the societies made one of their collective tasks. "I possess only the same general interest in the subject of geography that should be felt by every educated man," proclaimed Gardiner Greene Hubbard.[10] But what if the other men were neither as well educated nor as instinctively curious? How could they become stimulated? The *National Geographic Magazine* might engage the attention of laymen, but for the most part other journals would be read only by practitioners of the particular disciplines. Lester Ward was reminded of this when he was told that "such writings as yours are the leaven, a very little of which ultimately affects the whole mass, but for my present purposes I cannot wait for the bread to 'rise.' "[11]

Fortunately, there was a technique that offered immediate results: programs geared specifically to non-professional audiences. During the eighties and nineties most groups attempted popular lectures and demonstrations. The Anthropological and Biological Societies offered introductory courses at the Smithsonian; the National Geographic gave several lectures illustrated by maps, lantern slides, and stereoptic views; and the Chemical held a public exhibition of "liquid air" at the Columbian University.[12] Thus the new societies tended to utilize the same methods for kindling popular appreciation just as they had for advancing their own specialities.

Besides generating enthusiasm, these parallel efforts and common undertakings accelerated a movement to unify all the societies. Two years after leaving the presidency of the Cosmos Club, Charles D. Walcott noted a heightened awareness that "a central, well-organized representative body can be of great assistance to individuals and groups of workers in different ways, particularly in helping to arouse public interest in scientific investigations and in directing it to the best ends." Though it started gradually, by the end of the century Washington's intellectual community experienced a concerted drive to "bring within one organization the leading persons representing scientific activities at the National Capital." [13]

The first hints that Washington's scientific organizations were heading toward some sort of federated status came in the early eighties. Each year marked a perceptible step closer to union, but progress was slow. In the spring of 1882 the Philosophical Society suggested that it send representatives to confer with delegates from the Anthropological and Biological Societies to discuss consolidation of the three into a "central academy of sciences, with sections devoted to the several departments of science."[14] Two lengthy meetings resulted in a prospectus of an organization to be known as the Washington Academy of Sciences. While the affiliated retained their separate identities, the Academy would be responsible for a common publication of transactions, arranging sessions of the united societies, the election of its own officers and honorary fellows, collecting membership fees, and conducting series of popular lectures. [15]

Popular lectures were repugnant to the Philosophical Society, however, and the organization which initiated the conference ended-up vetoing its recommendations. Yet this did not mean that the Philosophical was averse to institutional cooperation, and the next year it invited members of the other societies to attend its annual meeting, thus establishing a precedent of joining together to hear each other's presidential addresses. Also, in 1884, the Philosophical participated in a joint reception for the Society of Eastern Naturalists during that group's Christmas convention in Washington. Such professional connections contributed to the advancement of science and were perfectly consistent with the Philosophical's character and purpose. But staging simplified programs for the uniniated fell outside this category, and, in 1886, when the Biological and Anthropological

Societies asked the Philosophical if it would assist "in the management and control of the Saturday Lectures," the latter respectfully declined. Its reasoning was that "if the scheme was a good one in itself it would be eminently proper that the scientific men in Washington should execute it."[16] "Scientific men" was the operative phrase here, a code expression for professional purity, and since that was the essence of the Philosophical there was no chance that it would stoop to popular lectures. Though relations between the societies were cordial and joint functions common, a full-scale alliance remained out of the question.

Grove Karl Gilbert attributed this to "the conservatism of the governing body of . . . [the Philosophical] Society." Because he was a member of that governing body throughout the 1880's his statement bears the seal of authenticity. Taken at face value, however, it implies an obdurate refusal to participate in any mutual venture. Such an interpretation would be inaccurate. On the contrary, the Philosophical led the way in strengthening ties between the societies. Repeated objections to the Saturday Lectures did not indicate a hostility toward union; rather they illuminated the irreducible differences between an elitist conception of promoting science, and the view shared by the Anthropological and Biological Societies that the same end could be achieved through the encouragement of amateurs. This also happened to be Gilbert's view, and while a Philosophical Society stalwart, he continuously stressed the manifold advantages of spreading scientific information to the public as well as to practitioners. In 1900, he advised James McKeen Cattell, the new editor of the *Popular Science Monthly:*

> The popularization of science is a function which the scientific guild can not afford to neglect. Not only is it positively important to give attention to it in order that sufficient interest may be maintained to secure the continuous endowment of research, but it is negatively important to occupy a field which because it can be made profitable, is tempting to the charlatan.[17]

Like Gilbert, the Philosophical Society was four square against charlatanism. But it also could not countenance popularization, and so in the early eighties it stood apart from the federation movement. "Under these circumstances," concluded Gilbert and Whitman Cross, "there could be no merging of the societies without the surrender by the Philosophical of its exclusiveness, and the opponents of union were those members of the Philosophical Society who were unwilling to give its work a more popular character."[18]

By 1887, these distinctions between the Philosophical and the other groups were starting to blur. That was when the Cosmos Club became a headquarters for all the societies, and the *gemutlichkeit* it afforded helped make the Philosophical's leaders more amenable to change. In February of that year the scientific establishment was heartened to learn that "the Philosophical Society would probably be willing to cooperate in the Saturday Lectures during the present season. . . ."[19] When this occurred it opened the way for permanent federation. Once again, the organization which Gilbert labeled conservative was in the vanguard.

In fact, the impulse for cementing an alliance originated in the Philosophical Society. At the General Committee meeting of January 7, 1888, Marcus Baker offered a resolution proposing that each society designate three representatives, to confer as a body, "respecting the formation of a permanent organization to deal with questions of common interest to all these scientific societies."[20] Drawing attention to the rapid increase of specialized groups, Baker emphasized that the number of its siblings had multiplied to four. His concern was not so much with future growth—though certainly this must have been on his mind—but rather with giving the five societies a sense of mutual destiny. Others shared his sentiments and the resolution passed by a vote of eleven to eight. President Garrick Mallery appointed Robert Fletcher, W. H. Dall (subsequently replaced by Powell), and Baker to serve as spokesmen for the Philosophical Society.[21]

Similar actions were taken by the executive councils of the Anthropological, Biological, Chemical, and Geographic Societies, and on February 19, 1888, beneath the roof of the Cosmos Club, their delegations assembled for the first time. Eleven men attended this organizational meeting of what was at once christened the "Joint Committee." Fletcher and Baker were elected chairman and secretary, all affirmed support for the Philosophical Society's resolution, and it was agreed to convene again as soon as possible.[22] February twenty-fifth signified a day of fulfillment for those who doggedly had pursued the elusive goal of union. Finally it seemed within their grasp. Through an "organic act" the delegates created a permanent Joint Commission of the Scientific Societies of Washington. This was to consist of three commissioners from each organization who would perform a two-fold function. As stated in the original resolution the Joint Commission should give advice on "questions of common interest." But now it was invested with the additional authority to "execute instructions on general subjects. . . ." Such instructions were not to be binding and member societies could disregard the Joint Commission's will. At the

same time, however, this ambiguous clause suggested that the fathers of
the Joint Commission did not conceive of it as being peripheral to the scientific establishment. Without trying to predict how its influence should
later be applied, they equipped it for any eventuality. During the next six
weeks the organic act was ratified by the five component societies and the
Joint Committee adjourned *sine die*, its preparatory labors having come to
an end.[23]

Almost immediately the Joint Commission commenced operations. In
1889, it offered to invite the American Association for the Advancement of
Science, on behalf of the local societies, to hold its fortieth annual meeting
in Washington two years hence. When the AAAS accepted, the Joint
Commission suddenly took on stature as the host organization. Undis-
mayed by responsibilities of managing a national convention its committees set to work raising money, arranging transportation and hotel reservations, planning receptions and excursions, and making certain that the
entire affair received appropriate publicity. An eight-man executive
committee, "with full power to act for the Commission," was created as a
coordinating unit which also dealt with Frederick Ward Putnam, permanent secretary of the AAAS. The meeting lasted for over two weeks, during which time the visitors heard scheduled papers and attended business
sessions at the Arlington Hotel and Columbian University, exchanged
information with foreign scientists (this marked the first time the International Congress of Geologists came to the United States), inspected the
public buildings and historic landmarks, and were entertained at a party
given by the Washington Board of Trade. Not only did everything go off
without a hitch, but the treasury reported a surplus of over $1,100. These
unexpended funds were to be used for the support of member societies. For
a while the Joint Commission was able to dispense largesse commensurate
with its new found importance.[24]

After this initial burst of activity, however, the Joint Commission settled into a role that was largely symbolic. It seldom advised or instructed,
as the organic act provided for, and it was hardly the decisive force in
government-science that some of its creators expected it would become.
When the societies began meeting at the Cosmos Club, in 1887, the Joint
Commission donated a common specimen cabinet to the assembly hall,
but it could not follow through on a proposal to establish a joint library for
the use of its affiliates.[25] Expansion was undertaken with extreme caution
and there was no concerted drive to consolidate all specialized groups. The
Microscopical Society was barred entirely, and the Entomological

Society, founded in 1884, was not granted a seat on the Joint Commission until December, 1892.

On the other hand, no time was wasted in publishing a *Directory of Scientific Societies of Washington*. Appearing biennially, from 1889 to 1895, it contained single lists of the names and addresses of all society members. This obviated the need for separate brochures and, because many individuals belonged to two or more groups, solved the problem of duplication. The *Directory* also constituted a sign of nominal integration and the Joint Commission's meetings, held every month or two, kept open channels of communication between the various organizations. Beyond this it could boast of few concrete accomplishments.

Yet the Joint Commission had a certain value occrued from intangible assets. Its mere being assured the affiliated members of the maturity of Washington's professional elite. As with other self-conscious groups that were emerging and asserting themselves at this time an overarching association seemed *prima facie* evidence of coming of age. Regardless of their operational effects, late nineteenth century structures conveyed the impression of robustness. Their true authority might be limited, or their jurisdiction circumscribed, or their capital watered, or their literal resources exaggerated—nonetheless, their institutional forms symbolized power, especially to those who identified with them. Central aggregations meant quantity, and quantity was taken to represent growth and development. Thus commissioners were predisposed to equate the proliferation of specialized bodies with the general association's progress: "Only twenty-two years have passed, and Washington has become the most important scientific center in the Americas—twenty-two years, and instead of one society we have six. . . ."[26] (Presumably a doubling of this figure would bring world-wide supremacy.) So the net worth of the Joint Commission was the confidence and self-esteem it inspired, not through its actions but simply by its existence.

Similarly, the Joint Commission helped improve the quality of local culture and bestowed status and prestige on its members. Neither was easily verified, though many scientists intuitively felt that these influences issued from its presence. Sensing vaguely that the Joint Commission had a positive affect on themselves and their community, they resorted to forms of expression that seemed unscientific. Garrick Mallery, in a bit of topical verse, plumbed the depth of its contribution and concluded that before the Civil War "every congressman thought he could boss over a fellow who was merely a philosopher," while afterward "a Joint Commission of societies saved science and restored the lost proprieties." In addition, men of rarefied taste, to whom Gilded Age culture was generally unappetizing, could derive sustenance from the organization:

> What though our formal dinner may be horrid,
> The soup be frigid and the salad torrid,
> Though then your palate gets not full fruition,
> You have some pablum in your Commission;
> We're fit to eat, -- if doubting, only try it--
> Our body's in a double sense your Diet![27]

In the main Mallery was correct, and certainly his metaphor evoked the ethos of the Joint Commission. After savoring this morsel, however, one suspects that before the "pabulum" could become a satisfactory "diet" it would have to be seasoned liberally.

Some of the Joint Commission's leaders must have been left with the same impression for in 1895 they undertook to make it more effective. At its first meeting of the year President Gardiner Hubbard called for an open discussion of the organization's condition. Nearly all the commissioners voiced opinions about how it might be improved and there seemed to be a consensus in favor of "combining the scientific societies more closely along lines of common interest." Distributing joint notices of sessions and collaborating on a monthly publication were motions which received wide support. Before going ahead with any plan, however, it was decided to accept Otis Mason's proposal that the presidents of the societies comprise a committee "on the State of the Union." The committee's report began with the premise that further cooperation depended on "enlarging the power of the Joint Commission." This meant providing it with enough administrative machinery to become a governing body, giving it the same sort of institutional framework as the professional groups of which it was composed, in short, making it more than a figurehead. Accordingly, the next six weeks witnessed the adoption of a constitution and a set of by-laws.[28]

These documents increased the size of the Joint Commission and broadened the margins of its activity. Instead of having just three delegates from each of the societies (excepting the Entomological and Geological which had fewer seats due to their small memberships) it would henceforth be made up of all their officers and board members. Consequently the organization which previously numbered eighteen now had a grand total of ninety-three participants. Since this was too unwieldy to conduct business, the constitution provided for an eleven man executive committee. Herein lay responsibility for all policies and administrative details, and though its decisions were subject to review at the Joint Commission's annual meetings, its rule was virtually absolute. The committeemen were the president and secretary of the Joint Commission, as well as those holding the newly created offices of vice-president and treasurer, and one member at large from each component society. Their terms were for twelve months without prohibitions against reelection.

Obviously the Joint Commission's government weighed more heavily than before, the result of its operations having become more ample. In place of its almost non-existent advisory functions, the revamped body was empowered to organize joint meetings, continue the *Directory* on an annual basis, distribute composite meeting notices for the several groups, hold lectures, and "to act in the interest of the component societies at the instance of any of them." These last provisions were implemented when the Joint Commission, at the request of the Geological Society, sponsored Sir Archibald Geikie's address during the famed British scientist's visit to Washington in 1896.[29] The Joint Commission also might cause itself to meet specially upon request of the president or any ten commissioners. If the contours of this design seemed familiar it was because most of them were the work of Major Powell, whose bold strokes were easily recognized.[30]

The reorganization of 1895 made the Joint Commission more comprehensive, but not everyone considered this an unqualified good. Broader powers for the central body, said its opponents, might result in actions which would be counterproductive for the separate societies. Responding to this apprehension, seven of the eighteen officers of the Philosophical Society voted to maintain the status quo.[31] For one thing they felt that the existing machinery was good enough; that the psychological consequences it produced were satisfactory and that the so-called "common interests" of the several societies were insufficient to warrant a major overhaul. There were also expressions of alarm about what a more energetic association might do. Without implying that the Joint Commission would fall into the hands of reckless men, they placed enough credence in Lord Action's famous dictum concerning the corrupting effects of power to be somewhat chary. One of their concerns had to do with the likelihood of unforseen expenses, a concern which proved well-founded in 1897 when the Joint Commission almost went broke.[32] However, it was not the Philosophical Society, a large and solidly established group, which registered the first complaints against fiscal policies, but rather the Chemical Society, whose weaknesses at that time left it vulnerable to any added strain.

Under its constitution, Joint Commission expenditures were to be borne by the component groups in proportion to their memberships. With only 116 members in 1896 (before suddenly acquiring all the city's members of the American Chemical Society) the Chemical Society was Washington's second smallest professional organization. The amount it paid into the common treasury was correspondingly slight, but viewed from the srand-point of its own resources this represented over 35% of its income. Moreo-ver, the Chemical Society was not getting much for its money. Since its annual meetings were sparsely attended there was no need of holding them under the auspices of the Joint Commission, and the master schedules of meetings which the Joint Commission issued were deemed to be of limited value. Therefore, its Executive Committee submitted a series of resolu-tions to the several societies proposing that the Joint Commission's power to prepare and distribute programs be reduced. Each organization should send out whatever notices it chose to publicize rather than having them all compiled in blanket announcements. Also, instead of every member of every society automatically receiving notices, those who were interested in attending another's meetings must ask for invitations and include return postage with their requests.[33] The axe being ground had an economic appearance, particularly because the Chemical Society of Washington received financial aid from the American Chemical Society which also was trying to hold down expenses. Yet the root of the problem lay deeper than that, for men with individual grievances were also having second thoughts about the way they had been yoked together.

Due to the fact that in activities it surpassed the original version, the new Joint Commission stood condemned for having attempted too much. At the same time it was criticized for not doing enough for Washington's scientists of distinction. Ironically the first Joint Commission — those honored by their societies to serve as representatives — had been more nota-ble for the prestige it conferred than the policies it enacted. After 1895, however, it consisted of the officers of the societies, meaning that commis-sioners were determined in the same perfunctory way that men were elected in their components. While this process ran smoothly it was devoid of gradeur. When Arnold Hague observed that the Joint Commission represented *societies* instead of *scientists* he touched the nub of the issue: to the city's most brilliant minds it was utterly boring. The very designa-tion of "commission" connoted organizational dullness, with its ranks having a caste of administrative rather than technical accomplishment. For the most part commissioners were business managers and, "As it is frequently the case that the men who are most prominent in scientific work

are for one reason or another reluctant to give time to the affairs of societies," many of the best government-scientists were left outside. Not that
they really wanted to get in, since association with the Joint Commission
carried little professional significance. This inability to satisfy legitimate
desires for recognition prompted efforts to make the central body less
powerful and more honorific.[34]

During the first third of 1897 the Geological Society conducted an
inquiry into the background and current operations of the federation, and
in conclusion expressed "its disapproval of the present organization of the
Joint Commission as being neither well adapted for performing the business of the societies nor representing them in scientific matters."[35] But
how devise a union which could balance between general effectiveness and
acceptability to all components; which might conduct business and bestow
honor; which would possess the advantages of both form and substance?
This the Geological Society did not presume to know. Instead, on September 15, 1897, it suggested in a circular letter that each society appoint three
men to another conference committee to seek the best possible solution.
For the third time in nine years there would be an attempted merger of
Washington's men of science. At its second meeting the conferees unanimously resolved that some form of "federal head, competent to initiate
action," was desirable, but that the "autonomy of the several scientific
societies should be maintained." It was imperative that the central organization have a scientific character and be representative in scientific as well
as in business matters. To this end the committee recommended that the
Joint Commission "assume independent scientific functions, have power
to add to its members," and that it be given a more imposing title.[36] The
move to make the Joint Commission less objectionable thus culminated
with a call for an entirely new institution, a Washington Academy of Sciences.

Nothing could have been more gratifying to those who bent every effort
to advance science and culture at the national Capital. Having launched
half a dozen organizations for the promotion of different specialties they
now looked forward to completing the fusion of these bodies into a more
vital union. Small wonder that discussions about the proposed academy
engaged the soaring imaginations of its principal founders. Powell talked
of an association which would combine exclusiveness and financial stability by imposing a minimum fee on the members of component societies,
with a select group for whom the dues would be higher. Gilbert envisioned
the Academy becoming the agency of popularization—giving lectures and
attracting patrons— so that the societies could grapple with the frontiers of

knowledge in their particular disciplines. McGee saw it as an instrument of harmony, respecting the specialized jurisdictions of the societies while working for the accomplishment of mutual objectives. Specifically this meant the further development of Washington's intellectual community.[37]

Powell, Gilbert, and McGee were among the fifteen men appointed by the Joint Commission to draft a constitution. Others included C. Hart Merriam, an officer in the Biological and National Geographic; L. O. Howard representing the Biological and Entomological Societies; Arnold Hague from the Geological; H. N. Stokes the Chemical; John Robie Eastman, F. W. Clarke, Bernard Green, and Marcus Baker the Philosophical; and Frank Baker, George M. Sternberg, and Lester Frank Ward from the Anthropological. Ward and Sternberg were also vice-presidents in the Philosophical Society whose numerical superiority totaled almost half the committee. In order to expedite its mission two subcommittees were assigned responsibility for drafting working documents. Eastman, Merriam, and Clarke set to work outlining functions of the Academy, and Green, Frank Baker, and Powell criteria for its membership.[38] The urgency of these matters was attested to by the prompt consideration they received. On January 15, 1898, just four days after being formed, the subcommittees filed their reports.

Concentrating on the twin objectives of elitist control and broad representation, Powell's group prescribed a formula for achieving both. This entailed four membership categories: regular members, fellows, honorary members, and patrons. The first classification was open to anyone in a component who paid dues to the Washington Academy, thereby integrating the affiliated societies and guaranteeing the central body economic support. Moreover, it served as a mechanism for gradual expansion and gave each member a personal stake in the Academy's future. But direct participation was restricted to those in the next and far more important category, the fellows, who "shall have power to add to their members and in their hands shall rest the government of the Academy."

The "nucleus," as this elite was properly called, was to constitute the vital essence of the organization. Initially its composition would follow from the components balloting "for the fifty persons whom they consider best qualified." The report did not define "best qualified," an omission making it possible to vote for either top-flight scientists or administrators. By splitting the difference between the Philosophical and the specialized societies, Powell's draft became acceptable to all parties. Also, once formed, the nucleus would fill its own vacancies. The way was thus cleared for the same sort of centralization of power and continuity of personnel that had given stability to the components. In addition, the fellows chose honorary members, "persons distinguished in science, literature or art," and presumably it was through their policies that patrons would be acquired. Except for changes of detail—enlarging the nucleus to seventy-five and having electors vote for one hundred men, the twenty-five lowest vote-getters being eliminated; dropping "literature or art" from the qualifications for honorary membership; and reducing the classes of members to three—the report won a favorable reception.[39]

The adoption of an organizational blueprint spurred further action, and within the next sixty days the Washington Academy was created and the Joint Commission permanently dissolved. On January nineteenth C. Hart Merriam, speaking for the constitutional committee, proposed that steps be taken to incorporate the new body under the laws of the District of Columbia. While this was being accomplished the seventy-five members of the nucleus were elected, their names to be kept secret until the first meeting was announced. One of the Joint Commission's last acts was accepting as an affiliate the Medical Society of the District of Columbia, thus permitting the eighty year old association to become a founder of the Academy even though it had not participated in informing the intellectual community. Finally an incorporation draft and a set of by-laws were submitted to the eight components.[40] These ratification meetings were witness to more quibbling over minor points in the instruments of government (once again the Chemical Society had reservations about the levying of assessments), but all agreed that such a government was both desirable and necessary. Some members of the Anthropological Society would have preferred a local version of the AAAS, a single organization with the membership divided into separtate sections, but this did not cause them to oppose the plan under consideration. The Chemical Society pushed Dr. Harvey Wiley's resolution that the governing board be made up of the affiliates' executive committees. Though this was rejected out of hand by the Joint Commission, the Chemical Society continued to back the unionists. Illustrative of the concensus favoring the Academy was the ratification vote taken in the Philosophical Society. Whereas in 1888 almost half of its General Committee opposed establishing the Joint Commission, and in 1895 over one-third was against strengthening it, now only a single negative ballot was cast.[41] When the members-elect held their initial meeting they did so with near unanimous support from the scientific establishment. John Robie Eastman, G. K. Gilbert, and Bernard R. Green were chosen president, secretary, and treasurer, to be joined subsequently by eight vice-presidents, each representing his own component. On March twenty-second the Joint Commission passed out of existence and these men became the official leaders of the intellectual community, in the name of the Washington Academy of Sciences.[42]

That the by-laws and act of incorporation would be accepted was almost a foregone conclusion, since the membership sub-committee borrowed principles of internal structure from the specialized societies. Much less certain was the fate in store for the draft of functions which harkened back to a plan that had already been rejected. The second sub-committee's report seemed a replica of the abortive 1882 plan of union, and though there was only one member of the constitutional committee (Powell) who had a hand in composing the original version, the current proposals resoundingly echoed those of sixteen years before. Proclaiming "the promotion of science" as the Academy's purpose, the sub-committee on functions said that this could be effected by courses of lectures, holding joint sessions, publishing and distributing a directory and joint notices of meetings, abetting research and investigation in any way, securing a permanent building, and by cooperating "with existing scientific and other societies in matters of common concern.[43]

Considering that this concept had once died aborning what hope was there for survival now? In the first place the Philosophical Society no longer discountenanced popular programs. After having thrown its weight behind the Saturday Lectures in 1887, the Society now went along with efforts for greater cooperation. Unlike the other organizations its General Committee did not unanimously endorse the reorganization of 1895, but neither did it threaten to boycott the Joint Commission's expanded activities. Secondly, the prospect of a Washington Academy held out enticing advantages to all concerned. Not only would it serve as a kind of interlocking directorship for the various organizations but it also promised to take over the task of popularization, allowing the societies to make their meetings more technical and to devote their attention to more challenging topics. In collaboration with these groups it would help advance national science, and its own activities would carry forward the improvement of local culture.

Lectures for laymen had traditionally been the shortest route to inspiring a general appreciation for science—especially during periods of rapid social and economic change when "cultivation" was in vogue. From the vantage point of the Gilded Age, therefore, Washington's savants could fully comprehend the appeal of earlier popularizers. Before the Civil War Benjamin Silliman was among the most skillful if not the first practitioner of the art of presenting science to the public. His technique involved pain-staking rehearsals of lectures so that at the podium he would not be bound to his notes, making certain beforehand that experiments and illustrative demonstrations were sure to work, and then elucidating his subject with dignity and animation. As his fame spread the crowds increased, both in size and zeal, so that it became customary for people to arrive hours ahead of time in order to get good seats. For over twenty years, from Buffalo to Mobile and between Nantucket and Pittsburgh, the Yale professor deci-phered the mysteries of geology and chemistry for large gatherings. Silli-man considered these performances his highest service to science. They also netted him a handsome income, raised funds for educational estab-lishments such as the Lowell Institute, and, in the words of a disciple, "attracted to his lectures the refined and cultivated."[44] What Silliman did for physical science was matched by Louis Agassiz in biology. Droves of men and women listened approvingly as he described the complex magnif-icance of creation, with both Agassiz and his audiences feeling ennobled by the experience. The lesson was not lost on his friend Joseph Henry who was seeking ways of advancing and diffusing knowledge through the Smithsonian Institution. Henry could not hope to duplicate Agassiz's "charming Continental accent,"[45] but it was possible to copy his method for whetting the public's appetite. Thus, in the 1850's "the best feature of Washington was the courses of lectures given at the Smithsonian, not lim-ited to science, which enabled us to hear eminent educators from various parts of the country."[46] In 1882 the Smithsonian again became the scene of popular lectures, only this time they were sponsored by Washington's new scientific societies.

The history of the Saturday Lectures provides a gauge for measuring the intellectual community's development in the eighties and nineties. At first there were sharp differences over whether Washington societies were cut out for this sort of activity. In contrast to the Anthropological and Biological Societies, the Philosophical maintained that responsibility for lectures resided with the Smithsonian Institution.[47] Once this argument had been irrefutable, but the rise of new societies deflected its thrust since they were so strongly committed to popularization. Also, popularizers were sustained by the Smithsonian's assistant secretary who proclaimed it "the duty of every scientific scholar, however minute his specialty," to help kindle enthusiasm. Indeed scientists had a solemn obligation to fur-ther the broadest possible education of non-professionals.[48] But here, as in other matters, the Joint Commission was only moderately successful, and not for several years did the Saturday Lectures acquire a definite place in the intellectual life of the city. When they did, however, it signaled the revitalization and public significance of local bodies. In 1897 Cleveland Abbe wished some programs could be delivered "in the Senate Chamber, to Congress—it would be an admirable improvement on the ordinary methods of lobbying."[49] Though the proposal itself may have been only half-serious, Abbe was correct in implying that distillation and transmission of general knowledge reflected the potency of Washington's scientific establishment.

Lectures were usually considered from the standpoint of public enlightenment rather than in terms of how they strengthened the institutions which sponsored them. On the occasion of the first Saturday meeting, held March 11, 1882, Powell announced that the ensuing series was designed to offer "birds-eye views to inquiring students," and that audiences could anticipate learning "the simpler lessons taught by the works of nature."[50] In 1893, following a three year lapse, the annual courses were renewed on the grounds that they served to introduce laymen to science. Later the Washington Academy's Committee on Functions not only assumed responsibility for arranging lectures, it also strove to expand them by sending special notices to public school teachers. Programs would now be "more serviceable," justifying honorariums for speakers.[51] Because of their public character and educational purpose, W J McGee likened the Saturday Lectures to a "university extension," to the kind of institution "which has attracted so much interest in other portions of the country within the last five years."[52]

Viewed through McGee's lense, the Saturday Lectures transcended their own time and place, and took on a much richer historical meaning. They magnified the Washington Academy's key transitional position between such pioneers of professionalization as Benjamin Peirce, Alexander Dallas Bache, and Louis Agassiz, and the modern university in which professionalization would ultimately be achieved. In 1851, Agassiz, Peirce, and James Hall had endeavored to launch at Albany, New York the national university which they recognized as indispensible to the progress of professional science. Their efforts failed for want of adequate financial backing, however, and by 1853 it was clear that the national university would have to await a more propitious moment and a more favorable setting. Agassiz next invoked the idea in 1862, when he suggested to Governor John A. Andrew of Massachusetts that the state take control of Harvard University (the College would remain a private and—feared Agassiz—a hopelessly retarded institution), secure federal subsidies under the Morrill land-grant college legislation, and thereby fill the need for "a

real University in the United States . . . an institution . . . offering information of the highest character upon every topic of human knowledge and so
superior to all other institutions that students from every part of the country would flock to it." Once again, the scheme was not acted upon. Indeed
it was so ambitious that its entire scope was never made public.[53]

McGee's 1894 allusion echoed the spirit of Agassiz's aims, except that
it harkened back to a longer standing tradition and enjoyed the support of
a more solidly founded intellectual community. He dreamed not just of a
national university, but of a great center of learning at the seat of government. This objective was almost as old as the nation itself, and from the
days of Benjamin Rush and George Washington onward, it had attracted
impressive endorsements. But it never proved compelling enough to be
translated into reality.[54] At the opening of the nineteenth century, Joel
Barlow had urged the creation of "a national university at the federal city," an institution of "public instruction" that would be "of much
more extensive and various utility than anything that has hitherto
existed. . . ."[55] His *Prospectus* delineated a chancellor, a professorate
"divided into about five or six classes according to their pursuits," a board
of trustees, museums of art and natural history, a national library, a
school of medicine, an observatory, and free weekly lectures. Key to all
this would be "associations of scientific men," whose appreciation for
collecting and disseminating knowledge would give direction to the whole
educational project.[56] As G. Brown Goode noted in 1890, "Although
Barlow's plan was, in its details much too elaborate for the times, the
fundamental ideas were exceedingly attractive, and led to very important
and far-reaching results."[57]

By the close of the century, these results were being manifested through
the reigning confidence among Washington intellectuals that something
approximating Barlow's plan was on the verge of being redeemed. In large
measure this optimism fulfilled their own exuberance. Those concerned
with transforming the political Capital into a city of cultural excellence
showed little hesitancy about enlisting in the crusade. Horatio King was on
a committee which exhorted Congress to incorporate an institution under
the government, Joseph Henry became involved with the National University Committee of scientists and educators, and, in 1884, The Literary's
president used his inaugural to stress the "taste and culture manifested in
the society of Washington and the suitability of that city as a site for a
great National University."[58]

Meanwhile, there was a movement afoot to upgrade Columbian University, an effort further demonstrating the enthusiasm for making Washing-

ton an educational base. Without endowments, but having the support of such local talent as Lester Frank Ward, who held the chair of botany, James Welling started the Corcoran Scientific School. This was a noble venture, though no substitute for a genuine University of the United States. Therefore, in 1891, when the American Association for the Advancement of Science met in Washington, Ward added his voice to the chorus demanding a center of higher learning. His design was laid out so that the end result would be "exclusively the product of the federal government," thus relying upon Congress for its enactment.[59] Others, mindful of official lethargy and undaunted by the pitfalls of an independent course, asked "is it not practicable to organize it [the instruction] under the Joint Committee of the Scientific Societies of Washington?"[60]

In reply a fair question might have been: what grounds were there for believing that the Joint Commission could make a success of such a project? It was understandable that men immersed in national science should seek to hasten the day when Washington would house a university operating in conjunction with technical agencies of the government. Furthermore, it was natural for those committed to the diffusion of knowledge as well as its creation to work unsparingly for the marriage of specialized research and general education. But even after making these allowances was it not presumptous to tie such a grand objective to local organization? It would have been except for the intellectual establishment's tempering of optimism with a keen awareness of its own resources. The enduring hope was that congress would recognize the wisdom of their vision, but failing this, government-scientists were prepared to utilize the existing machinery for disseminating learning. "We could reorganize the old Saturday Lectures on a higher plane in the lecture room of the National Museum," suggested Otis Mason, thereby improving the quality of instruction already being offered.[61]

Operating on such a scale the Joint Commission— and even more so the Washington Academy after 1898—could meet an interim need until the national university was established. Its educational mission was therefore regarded not as an ultimate solution, but rather as a beginning.

This signifies a kind of finality. By its vigor and self-assurance, the Washington Academy announced that the intellectual community's formative period was ended. The process that began with a series of groping attempts to impose order upon Gilded Age society, and which quickly meshed with the movement to promote government-science, had culminated in an institution dedicated to improving national culture. On one level it could be celebrated as the consummate expression of cultivation and elegance, with these attributes being shared by the Capital City. In another sense it was appreciated as the fruition of Washington's scientific establishment. The stature of its membership towered above those of the genteel circles, and as an agent for the advancement of science it surpassed even Henry's Philosophical Society. The Washington Academy of Sciences accommodated both amateurs and professionals. Its components represented specialization and they diffused technical knowledge, while the Academy itself, through public lectures, served the cause of popularization. Its structural form enabled it to bestow prestige on members and also function as an administrative body. In short, the Academy gave conclusive evidence of a flourishing intellectual community at the seat of government.

The formation of this community was only one of countless accomplishments of the post-Civil War period. But because its leaders figured in so many of these creative influences it occupied a special place in late nineteenth century culture. The Henrys, the Powells, the McGees, the Bairds, the Fletchers, the Newcombs, and the Wards were responsible for a host of bureaus, research institutions, and government enterprises which left lasting imprints on American life. In going about their work, these individuals revealed previously neglected sources of national strength, and by opening new areas of inquiry they enlarged the possibilities for future progress. Some of their most momentous achievements came when they thrust themselves into public service, for this gave the scientists and scholars representation in the realm of practical affairs. Here was an intellectual elite which sought not detachment, but influence; and to a significant degree its quest was fulfilled.

As for the future, the role of Washington's intellectual community was not entiely clear, since taken literally its work seemed to be done. One of the primary contributions had been to hasten the professional growth of certain sciences. Yet the twentieth century would find the university becoming the vital center of professionalization with Washington's scientists slipping to a secondary importance. Its commitment to retaining a place for the amateur in science appeared to be a lost cause, and this boded to turn the intellectual community into an anachronism, a throwback to the nineteenth century ethos of genteel culture. In May 1902, W J McGee, while serving as acting president of the National Geographic Society and hoping to bolster the Society's credibility in the world of higher learning, invited Harvard physical geographer William M. Davis to accept an associate editorship of the *National Geographic*. The professor spurned McGee's offer, writing at the bottom of the letter, "Declined: couldn't approve general policy of popularization at expense of science."[62] This terse response conveyed a prophetic message—that the march of academic professionalization had passed Washington by, leaving behind it the great days of the intellectual community as a force in the development of professional science and cultural institutions. Four months later John Wesley Powell was dead, as if symbolizing the drawing to a close of the intellectual community's vital period.

In the last analysis, however, the meaning of these clubs and societies transcends the time and place of their first leaders. As late nineteenth century organizations, they gave coherence and collective integrity to a cross section of individuals seeking influence in national life. But the ultimate significance of this intellectual community had been to exemplify the constant need for intelligence informed by social conscience: here is the real desideratum in Washington and the continuing challenge to every humane civilization.

Reviewing the early history of this community reminds one again of the Cosmos Club addresses of Henry Allen Moe and Louis Booker Wright. Their words come back like a whispered refrain: national culture can best be advanced by a particular kind of intellectual elite. The creators of Washington's establishment three-quarters of a century earlier would have appreciated this message, just as Moe and Wright were inspired by their example. Physically, these tightly-buttoned ladies and high-collared gentlemen belong to another age, but their spirit is timeless. Fittingly then, "an aristocracy of brains and character, an aristocracy with a conscience and a sense of history," serves both as an epitaph and as a tribute to their enduring vision.

NOTES TO CHAPTER 6

1. C. V. Riley, "Proceedings of the Four-Hundredth Meeting of the Philosophical Society of Washington," *Bulletin of the Philosophical Society of Washington,* XII (1892-1894), 557.

2. Minutes of the Council, February 21, 1893, Archives of the Geological Society of Washington, United States Geological Survey Library (henceforth GSW Archives, USGS); Whitman Cross and G. K. Gilbert, *Report of a Committee from the Geological Society on the History of the Joint Commission of the Scientific Societies of Washington* (Washington, D.C., 1897), p. 2.

3. *Proceedings of the Entomological Society of Washington,* I (1884), 5.

4. Minutes of the Council, February 11, 1881, Archives of the Biological Society of Washington, I, Division of Mammals, Smithsonian Institution (henceforth BSW Archives, SI).

5. Edward H. Beardsley, *The Rise of the American Chemistry Profession, 1850-1900* (Gainesville, Fla., 1964 [University of Florida Monographs, Social Sciences No. 23, Summer, 1964], pp. 27-28.

6. Edwin C. Buxbaum, *Collector's Guide to the National Geographic Magazine* (Wilmington, Del,. 1962), pp. 20-21.

7. Lester F. Ward to Othniel C. Marsh, May 4, 1898, Marsh Letterbooks, Peabody Museum Library, Yale University.

8. W J McGee, "The Work of the National Geographic Society," *National Geographic Magazine,* VII (August, 1896), 258-259.

9. McGee, *ibid.,* VII, 257.

10. Quoted in Buxbaum, *Collector's Guide,* pp. 18-19.

11. Samuel P. Langley to Lester F. Ward, December 19, 1890, Ward Papers, Autographs, III, 56, Brown University Library.

12. Annual Report of the Secretary, January 12, 1899, Archives of the Chemical

Society of Washington, in the custody of Charles L. Gordon, Bethesda, Md. (henceforth CSW Archives).

13. Charles D. Walcott to Edward W. Morley, January 9, 1900, Morley Papers, Box 3, Manuscript Division, Library of Congress (henceforth LC).

14. Minutes of the Council, April 14, 1882, BSW Archives, I, SI.

15. Report of Joint Committee of Conference, May 3, 1882, in G. K. Gilbert, "First Annual Report of the Secretary," *Proceedings of the Washington Academy of Sciences,* I (1899), 2-3.

16. Minutes of the Council, January 9 and February 20, 1886, BSW Archives, I, SI; Minutes of the General Committee, January 16, 30, and February 13, 1886, Philosophical Society of Washington Archives, United States Naval Research Laboratory (henceforth PSW Archives).

17. Quoted in Grover C. Batts, "The James McKeen Cattell Papers," *The Library of Congress Quarterly Journal of Current Acquisitions,* XVII (May, 1960), 171.

18. Cross and Gilbert, *Report of a Committee,* pp. 2-3.

19. Minutes of the Council, February 19, 1887, BSW Archives, II, SI; Minutes of the General Committee, February 21, 1887, PSW Archives.

20. Minutes of the General Committee, January 7, 1888, *ibid.*

21. March 31, 1888, *ibid.*

22. Minutes of the First Meeting of a Joint Committee, February 19, 1888, Minutes of Proceedings of the Joint Commission, Washington Academy of Sciences, Carnegie Institution Building, Washington, D. C. (henceforth WAS Archives; subsequent to my research the WAS Archives were transferred to the SI Archives).

23. Organic Act Creating Joint Commission of the Scientific Societies of Washington, *ibid.*

24. Minutes of the Joint Commission of Scientific Societies, January 17, February 5 and 14, March 6, and October 9, 1891, Minutes of Proceedings of the Joint Commission, WAS Archives; *Science,* XVIII (August 7, 1891), 71-72.

25. Minutes of the Joint Commission of Scientific Societies, November 26, 1894, *ibid.*

26. G. Brown Goode, "Proceedings of the Four-Hundredth Meeting of the Philosophical Society of Washington," *Bulletin of the Philosophical Society of Washington*, XII (1892-1894), 549.

27. Garrick Mallery, "Philosophical Phantasy," *ibid.*, 558-561.

28. Minutes of the Joint Commission of Scientific Societies, January 2 and 25, 1895, Minutes of Proceedings of the Joint Commission, WAS Archives.

29. Minutes of the Council, May 13, 1896, GSW Archives, USGS.

30. The Constitution and By-Laws first appeared in *Directory of Scientific Societies of Washington* . . ., V (1896), 10-12; for Powell's role in drafting the By-Laws see, Minutes of the Executive Committee, February 27 and March 12, 1895, Minutes of Proceedings of the Joint Commission, WAS Archives.

31. Minutes of the General Committee, February 16, 1895, PSW Archives.

32. Cross and Gilbert, Report of a Committee, pp. 7-8; an emphatic appeal "for furthering the common interests of the Scientific Societies of Washington" is Arnold Hague and C. W. Hayes to J. H. McCormick, September 15, 1897, Minutes of the Board of Managers, November 2, 1897, Records of the Anthropological Society of Washington, Box 5, National Anthropological Archives, Smithsonian Institution (henceforth ASW Records, SI); Minutes of the Executive Committee, December 14, 1897, Minutes of Proceedings of the Joint Commission, WAS Archives.

33. Charles E. Munroe and W. P. Cutter to J. H. McCormick, December 19, 1896, Minutes of the Board of Managers, January 12, 1897, Box 5, ASW Records, SI; Minutes of the Council, December 23, 1896, GSW Archives, USGS.

34. Arnold Hague and C. W. Hayes to J. H. McCormick, September 15, 1897, Minutes of the Board of Managers, November 2, 1897, Box 5, ASW Records, SI.

35. Minutes of the Council, May 26, 1897, GSW Archives, USGS; the tedious course of the investigation may be followed in the Minutes of January 27, February 24, and March 24, 1897, *ibid.*

36. Whitman Cross Report to the Chairmen of the Several Committees [comprising the Joint Commission's Committee of Conference], December 13, 1897, Scrapbook, WAS Archives.

37. Minutes of the Joint Commission of Scientific Societies, January 11, 1898, Minutes of Proceedings of the Joint Commission, *ibid.*

38. Minutes of the Committee on Constitution, January 11, 1898, *ibid.*

39. January 15 and 17, 1898, *ibid.*, and Minutes of the Joint Commission of the Scientific Societies, January 19 and 25, 1898, *ibid.*

40. January 19, 31, and February 2, 1898, *ibid.*

41. Minutes of the Board of Managers, February 15, 1898, Box 5, ASW Records, SI; Minutes of the Executive Committee, January 22, 1898, CSW Archives; Minutes of the General Committee, February 5, 1898, PSW Archives.

42. Minutes of the Joint Commission of Scientific Societies, March 22, 1898, Minutes of Proceedings of the Joint Commission, WAS Archives.

43. Minutes of the Committee on Constitution, January 15, 1898, *ibid.*

44. George P. Fisher, *Life of Benjamin Silliman* . . . (New York, 1866), I, 340; John F. Fulton and Elizabeth H. Thomson, *Benjamin Silliman, 1779-1864: Pathfinder in American Science* (New York, 1947), pp. 173-183.

45. Edward Lurie, *Louis Agassiz: A Life in Science* (Chicago, 1960), p. 127.

46. *Autobiography Memories and Experiences of Moncure Daniel Conway* (Boston, 1904), I, 210-211.

47. Minutes of the General Committee, February 13, 1886, PSW Archives.

48. G. Brown Goode, *The Beginnings of American Science, the Third Century* (Washington, D. C., 1888), p. 93.

49. Cleveland Abbe to Thomas C. Mendenhall, April 24, 1897, Mendenhall Papers, Box 6, American Institute of Physics.

50. J. W. Powell, "Introductory Address," *The Saturday Lectures* . . . *1882* (Washington, D. C., 1882), p. 2.

51. F. W. Clarke, Charles E. Munroe, and O. H. Tittman, "Report of Committee on Functions of the Washington Academy of Sciences," December 5, 1898, WAS Archives.

52. W J McGee to the editor of the Washington *News*, April 27, 1894, Correspondence, letterpress volume labeled, "Letters Sent to Speakers, March 5, 1892-October, 1895," Box 8, ASW Records, SI.

53. Lurie, *Agassiz*, pp. 180-182, 328-329.

54. David Madsen, *The National University: Enduring Dream of the USA* (Detroit, Mich., 1966), *passim*.

55. Joel Barlow to Thomas Jefferson, September 15, 1800, Jefferson Papers, CVII, Microfilm Reel 36, LC.

56. Joel Barlow, *Prospectus of a National University to be Established in the United States* (Washington, City, 1806), *passim;* Madsen, *National University*, pp. 46-50.

57. G. Brown Goode, "The Origin of the National Scientific and Educational Institutions of the United States," *Papers of the American Historical Association*, IV (1890), 28-29.

58. Minutes of the Literary Society of Washington, December 27, 1884, Literary Society Papers, I, LC.; P. J. Keene to Horatio King, December 24, 1870, King Papers, V, *ibid;* Joseph Henry to J. W. Hoyt, July 30, 1874, Henry Papers, XL, SI Archives.

59. L. F. Ward, "A National University . . .," *Science*, XVIII (1891), 281; James C. Welling to Lester F. Ward, September 13, 1886, Ward Papers, Autographs, II, 11, Brown University Library.

60. Edward S. Holden to Daniel C. Gilman, November 9 and 23, 1897, Gilman Papers, The Johns Hopkins University Library.

61. Otis T. Mason to the Members of the Anthropological Society of Washington, February 9, 1893, McGee Papers, Box 8, LC.

62. W J McGee to William Morris Davis, May 29, 1902, Harvard Geographical Institute Papers, Houghton Library, Harvard University.

Essay On Sources

The purpose of the essay that follows is to draw attention to the major source material used in this study. As regards manuscript and archival collections, the bibliography is complete. In the interest of brevity, however, only the most important published works and microfilmed dissertations have been selected for further mention. Also, there has been an attempt to avoid duplicating previously noted citations except where additional comments would prove helpful to the reader.

Archival and Manuscript Sources

As Edward Lurie has observed ("Some Manuscript Resources in the History of Nineteenth Century American Natural Science," *Isis,* XLIV [December, 1953], 363-370), an understanding of this period in the history of American science and its social relations must depend upon the utilization of manuscripts. This observation is borne out in studying the Washington intellectual community between 1870 and 1900. The most important collections of primary materials are in the archives of the several clubs and societies. Except in the cases of the Entomological and the National Geographic Societies, membership lists, minutes, reports, and correspondence files have been maintained and are open for inspection, though they are sometimes difficult for the researcher to locate. Hopefully these scattered collections will soon be transferred to the Archives of the Smithsonian Institution, thereby insuring their preservation and making them more accessible to scholars.

The Records of the Anthropological Society of Washington are housed in the National Anthropological Archives, the Smithsonian Institution. There are seventeen file boxes containing the Constitution and By-Laws;

171

Minutes of the Board of Managers (1895-1905) - unfortunately the earlier minutes have disappeared; Minutes of the Regular Meetings (1879-1896); Reports of the Curator, which include some letters; and six volumes of correspondence covering the years between 1880 and 1900. The volume labeled "Letters Sent to Speakers, March 5, 1892-October, 1895," has many W J McGee letters and is particularly informative. There is also a History File, but this is disappointingly thin. Supplementing the Records are correspondence files and annual and monthly reports in the Archives of the Bureau of American Ethnology, also located in the National Anthropological Archives. The correspondence files of the BAE are laced with communications pertaining to prominent figures in the Anthropological Society.

The Division of Mammals of the Smithsonian contains the archives of the Biological Society of Washington. The most significant of these are the three volumes of Council meeting minutes for the years between 1880 and 1906. The Biological Society records also include a copy of the original Constitution and Minutes of the Regular Meetings (1894-1907).

In lieu of an official depository, the archives of the Chemical Society of Washington are in the secretary's personal custody. Regrettably there are no extant Executive Committee minutes prior to 1898. There is, however, a volume of Annual Reports of Secretaries (1887-1913).

The richest source of unpublished information about the Cosmos Club is its History File, replete with typescript addresses to the members, newspaper clippings, reminiscences, and the "Recollections of Samuel Escue Tillman," a founder who worked with the Wheeler reconnaissances of the 1870's.

The United States Geological Survey Library contains archival material of the Geological Society of Washington. This includes single volumes of Council Minutes (1893-1900); the Minutes of Meetings (1893-1904); and two treasurers' Record Books (1893-1913 and 1896-1911).

Among the many important collections in the Manuscript Division of the Library of Congress is the Literary Society's Papers. Especially rewarding for the period before 1900 are Boxes 4 and 5, and those labeled "Various Publications," "Documents Relating to the History of the Society," and "Some Papers Presented at Meetings." In addition, there are two volumes of minutes, two volumes of the proceedings of the Executive Committee, and a volume of correspondence prior to 1925.

At the time they were consulted, the early records of the Philosophical Society were in the Division of Mathematics and Information Sciences, United States Naval Research Laboratory, Washington, D. C. They have since been moved to the Smithsonian Achives. Originally, they were arranged into four boxes of minutes and three boxes of correspondence, the former containing three red leather volumes of General Committee Minutes (1883-1911). Under the correspondence category is an undated box labeled "Material of Historical Interest," which has membership nominations and acceptances between 1871 and 1875. Handwritten drafts of Joseph Henry's communications to the Philosophical Society are in a folder marked "Addresses and Reports," in the Henryana File of the Smithsonian Institution Achives.

The Joint Commission of Scientific Societies and the Washington Academy of Sciences archives have also recently been relocated in the Smithsonian Institution Archives. Of primary interest are the Minutes of Proceedings of the Joint Commission of Scientific Societies of Washington (2 volumes). There is also a Scrapbook of Miscellaneous Printed Matter (1898-1922), and a folder labeled "Formation and Early History of the Academy," containing notices of meetings, nominations for membership, and reports of various committees.

Much data concerning Washington's intellectual community can be gleaned from the papers of government-scientists, local savants, persons of cultivation, and individuals associated with elegant circles and learned societies. The most fertile fields for this research are the Manuscript Division of the Library of Congress and the Smithsonian Institution Archives.

The following collections in the Library of Congress are of special relevance: The George F. Becker Papers, particularly the two boxes of General Correspondence containing letters from Samuel F. Emmons. The diaries of Edward M. Gallaudet yield insights into the day-to-day activities of the Washington establishment. Similarly, the diaries of James and Lucretia Garfield in the Garfield Papers (Boxes 2-5), shed light on the literary Society. The letters in volumes V-VII (1870-1883) of the Horatio King Papers provide the best history of King's literary reunions. The W J McGee Papers are indispensable to any study of scientific organizations during this period; its thirty-one containers house incoming and outgoing correspondence, scrapbooks, miscellaneous material, and articles and notes, with scarcely a dull item in the entire collection. The Anita Newcomb McGee Papers are disappointing on the Women's Anthropological Society of America, but facinating on the intellectual and social life of the Capital City. Simon Newcomb's papers contain revealing comments about the Cosmos Club. Included in the Joseph M. Toner Papers are fourteen boxes of letters, 1864-1896.

The major archival and manuscript holdings of the Smithsonian Institution, comprising a vast source of information regarding American culture in the nineteenth century, are described in Richard H. Lytle (ed.), *Preliminary Guide to the Smithsonian Archives* (Washington, D. C., 1971). Chief among these are the letters of Secretaries Joseph Henry (1846-1878), Spencer F. Baird (1878-1887), and Samuel P. Langley (1887-1906), which are organized generally according to official correspondence and private papers. Those in the first category relate to the diversified activities of the Institution, its administration and history. The private papers include carefully indexed autobiographical data, personal letters, and daily journals. Here may be found the diary kept by Henry's daughter, Mary, chronicling many key developments in national science. The official correspondence of the Institution also contains a volume of requests from Washington clubs and societies for the use of the lecture hall (1882-1890), and two folders with material pertaining to the national university movement (1870-1900). Finally, the projected fifteen volume published papers of Joseph Henry, now in progress under the general editorship of Nathan Reingold, will make available a wealth of information about nineteenth century Ameria.

Separate from the central Archives, but under the Smithsonian's jurisdiction, is the National Collection of Fine Arts Library, which has William Henry Holmes' "Random Records of a Lifetime, 1846-1931: Cullings, Largely Personal, from the Scrap Heap of Three Score Years and Ten, Devoted to Science, Literature and Art." Originally consisting of twenty volumes, the "personal" volumes (XVII-XX) have disappeared. What remains is an engrossing array of diary entries, field notes, typescript essays, letters, water colors, photographs, and other memorabilia collected by a man whose fifty years of public service kept him too busy to write his autobiography.

Other depositories with primary source material bearing upon the Washington intellectual community are: The American Philosophical Society (Franz Boas Papers and LeConte Family Papers); the Arthur and Elizabeth Schlesinger Library on the History of Women in America, Radcliffe College (Alice Cunningham Fletcher letters in the papers of Jane Gay Dodge); the Brown University Library (Lester Frank Ward Papers); the Burton Hisotorical Collection, Detroit Public Library (James McMillan Papers); Center for History and Philosophy of Physics, American Institute of Physics (Thomas Corwin Mendenhall's autobiographical notes, diary, and correspondence); the Henry E. Huntington Library and Art Gallery (the extensive William J. Rhees Collection, as well as letters of Clarence King and Horatio King); the Houghton Library, Harvard University (Papers of the Harvard Geographical Institute); The Johns Hopkins University Library (Daniel Coit Gilman Papers, Ira Remsen Papers, and Henry A. Rowland's correspondence with Mendenhall); the Massachusetts Historical Society (Theodore F. Dwight Papers); the Michigan Historical Collections (intermittent Gilman letters in the papers of James B. Angell, Thomas McIntyre Cooley, and Andrew C. McLaughlin); Museum of Comparative Zoology Archives, the Agassiz Museum. Harvard University (Alexander Agassiz Papers); the New-York Historical Society (volumes V and VI of the John Jay Knox Circular Letter); New York Public Library (Madeleine Vinton Dahlgren's daily record of household expenses and social calls); the Peabody Museum Library, Yale University (twenty-odd volumes of Othniel C. Marsh letterbooks); the Rutherford B. Hayes Library (correspondence of Mary Claflin, Stanley Matthews, William King Rogers, Rutherford B. Hayes, and xeroxed copies of "Washington Gossip," the *Cincinnati Commercial*, October 23, 1876-October 7, 1877); the Southwest Museum Library (Frank Hamilton Cushing Papers and Frederick W. Hodge Papers); and the University of Michigan Library (Samuel P. Langley letters and William Henry Holmes correspondence in the papers of Joseph B. Steere).

Published Diaries, Letters, Memories and Autobiographies

Thousands of Henry Adams' letters have been put into published form, some of the more useful compilations being: Newton Arvin (ed.), *The Selected Letters of Henry Adams* (New York, 1951); Harold Dean Cater (comp.), *Henry Adams and His Friends: A Collection of His Unpublished Letters* (Boston, 1947); Arthur Stanburrough Cook (ed.), "Six Letters of Henry Adams," *Yale Review,* X (October, 1920), 131-140; Worthington Chauncey Ford (ed.), *Letters of Henry Adams* (2 vols.; Boston, 1930-1938); Frederick Bliss Luquiens, "Seventeen Letters of Henry Adams," *Yale Review,* X (October, 1920), 111-130; and, for Marian Hooper Adams, Ward Thoron (ed.), *The Letters of Mrs. Henry Adams, 1865-1883* (Boston, 1936).

Other comments on post-Civil War culture appear in, Harry James Brown and Frederick D. Williams (eds.), *The Diary of James A. Garfield* (2 vols.; East Lansing, Mich., 1967); Mary L. Hinsdale (ed.), *Garfield-Hinsdale Letters: Correspondence Between James Abram Garfield and Burke Aaron Hinsdale* (Ann Arbor, Mich., 1949); Jackson I. Cope, "William James' Correspondence With Daniel Coit Gilman, 1877-

1881," *Journal of the History of Ideas,* XII (October, 1951), 609-627; Charles Richard Williams (ed.), *Diary and Letters of Rutherford Birchard Hayes, Nineteenth President of the United States* (5 vols.; Columbus, Ohio, 1922-1926), volumes III and IV; T. Harry Williams (ed.), *Hayes: The Diary of a President, 1875-1881* (New York, 1964); Allan Nevins and Milton Halsey Thomas (eds.), *The Diary of George Templeton Strong* (4 vols.; New York, 1952), especially volume IV for the 1865-1875 period; and Bernhard J. Stern (ed.), *Young Ward's Diary* (New York, 1935), covering Ward's first years in Washington.

Published letters relating to the history of science may be found in, Elmer Charles Herber (comp.), *Correspondence Between Spencer Fullerton Baird and Louis Agassiz—Two Pioneer American Naturalists* (Washington, D. C., 1963); LeRoy R. Hafen (ed.), *The Diaries of William Henry Jackson, Fronter Photographer* (Glendale, Calif., 1959), a particularly valuable source of information about F. V. Hayden; and, Carolyn Eisele, "The Charles S. Peirce-Simon Newcomb Correspondence," *Proceedings of the American Philosophical Society,* CI (October, 1957), 409-433, containing letters written between 1889-1894.

From the following reminiscences and self-portraits one can learn much about late nineteenth century life in Washington and the nation: *Charles Francis Adams, 1835-1915: An Autobiography* (Boston, 1916); David S. Barry, *Forty Years in Washington* (Boston, 1924); John Bigelow, *Retrospections of an Active Life* (5 vols.; New York, 1909-1913), volumes IV and V being most relevant; W. H. Crook, *Memories of the White House: The Home Life of Our Presidents from Lincoln to Roosevelt* (Boston, 1911); Julia B. Foraker, *I Would Live It Again: Memories of a Vivid Life* (New York, 1932); Daniel Coit Gilman, *The Launching of a University, and Other Papers: A Sheaf of Rememberances* (New York, 1906); L. A. Gobright, *Recollection of Men and Things at Washington During the Third of a Century* (Philadelphia, 1869); George F. Hoar, *Autobiography of Seventy Years* (2 vols.; New York, 1903); Henry Holt, *Garrulities of an Octogenarian Editor: With Other Essays Somewhat Biographical and Autobiographical* (Boston, 1923); E. D. Keyes, *Fifty Years' Observation of Men and Events, Civil and Military* (New York, 1884); Mrs. John A. Logan (ed.), *Thirty Years in Washington, or Life and Scenes in Our National Capital* (Hartford, Conn., 1901); Ward McAllister, *Society As I Have Found It* (New York, 1890); Simon Newcomb, *The Reminiscences of An Astronomer* (Boston, 1903); Mrs. Roger A. Pryor, *Reminiscences of Peace and War* (New York, 1904); Raphael Pumpelly, *My Reminiscences* (2 vols.; New York, 1918); and, *The Autobiography of Nathaniel*

Southgate Shaler, with a Supplementary Memoir by His Wife (Boston, 1909); Louis H. Sullivan, *The Autobiography of an Idea* (New York, 1924; Dover edn., 1956).

Henry Adams' *Democracy: An American Novel* (New York, 1880) is witty and penetrating; far more than the typical "Washington novel" of its day, if offers a profound vision of the American experience. Many of Henry Adams' trenchant *North American Review* articles of the late sixties and early seventies have been collected in, Charles Francis Adams, Jr. and Henry Adams, *Chapters of Erie* (Boston, 1871; Cornell paperback edn., Ithaca, N. Y., 1966) and, George Hochfield (ed.), *The Great Secession Winter of 1860-61, and Other Essays by Henry Adams* (New York, 1958); other important contemporary writings are, Elizabeth M. Chapin, *American Court Gossip* (Marshalltown, Ia., 1887); F.W.Clarke, "Science in Politics," *Popular Science Monthly,* XXVI (March, 1885), 577-586; John W. Draper, "Science in America," *Proceedings of the American Chemical Society,* I (1876-1878), 135-154, also appearing in *Popular Science Monthly,* X (1877), 313-326; G. Brown Goode, *The Museums of the Future* (Washington, D. C., 1891); J. Howard Gore, "Anthropology at Washington," *Popular Science Monthly,* XXXV (October, 1889), 786-795; Henry James, *Pandora* (1884), *The Novels and Tales of Henry James,* XVIII (26 vols.; New York, 1907-1917), while less biting than *Democracy* or *The Gilded Age,* is a marvelous satire of post-war Washington; William Van Rensseler Miller (ed.), *Select Organizations in the United States* (New York, 1894), includes Ward McAllister's, "Club and Society Life in the United States;" Arinori Mori, *Life and Resources in America* (Washington, D. C., 1871), offers an interesting perspective on the Gilded Age; Simon Newcomb, "Science and the Government," *North American Review,* CLXX (May, 1900), 666-678; C. S. Peirce, "The Place of Our Age in the History of Civilization," *Charles S. Peirce: Selected Writings,* ed. Philip P. Wiener (New York, 1966), 3-14; Henry S. Pritchett, "The Relation of Educated Men to the State," *Science, N.S.,* XII (November 2, 1900), 657-666; George Augustus Sala, *America Revisited* (New York, 1880); George Santayana, *Character and Opinion in the United States* (New York, 1920; Anchor edn., Garden City, N. Y., n.d.); Mark Twain and Charles Dudley Warner, *The Gilded Age: A Tale of Today* (2 vols.; Hartford, Conn., 1873).

Magazines, Newspapers, and Serial Publications

The journals of the various societies are valuable supplements to the previously described archives and manuscripts. Indeed, these publications might almost be considered primary sources because of the information they yield concerning the internal development of Washington's intellectual community. First, the *Transactions of the Anthropological Society of Washington,* I-III (1879-1885), which became the *American Anthropologist* in 1888; its counterparts are the *Proceedings of the Biological Society of Washington,* I-XIII (1880-1900); the *Bulletin of the Chemical Society of Washington,* I-IX (1884-1895); the *Proceedings of the Entomological Society of Washington,* I-IV (1884-1901); *Field and Forest,* I-III (1875-1878), the bulletin of the Potomac-Side Naturalists Club; the *National Geographic Magazine,* I-XI (1888-1900); the *Bulletin of the Philosophical Society of Washington,* I-XII (1871-1899); and, the *Proceedings of the Washington Academy of Sciences,* I (1899-1900). The publications of the Anthropological and Philosophical Societies, initially printed by the Smithsonian Institution, also appear in volumes of the *Smithsonian Miscellaneous Collections.*

Other specialized and general interest periodicals carried items pertaining to science and culture at the Capital City. For the emergence of the scientific community see: the *American Journal of Science and Arts* (after 1880, the *American Journal of Science);* the *Popular Science Monthly;* the *Proceedings of the American Association for the Advancement of Science; Science,* which maintained a weekly news column about Washington organizations; and, the *Annual Report of the Secretary to the Board of Regents of the Smithsonian Institution.* From time to time cultivated magazines printed articles about Washington intellectual life. The *Atlantic Monthly; Harper's New Monthly Magazine; Harper's Weekly; Lippincott's Monthly Magazine;* the *Nation;* the *North American Review;* and *Scribner's* are relevant in this regard. Also, interesting bits of information can be gathered from John Clagett Proctor's sketches of Washington clubs in the 1880's, which originally appeared in the Washington *Sunday Star* and are now in a compiled form at the Columbia Historical Society, Washington, D. C. The Washingtoniana Room of the Martin Luther King Memorial Library, Washington, D. C., has a complete holding of the Washington city directory *(Boyd's Directory of the District of Columbia).*

Historical Studies of Scientific Organizations

The secondary literature on Washington scientific societies during this period is virtually non-existent. Watson H. Monroe, *Scientific Institutions of Washington* (Washington, D. C., 1933), treats the community as a whole but makes no attempt to analyze the dynamics of the subject. The few articles dealing with components of the Washington Academy have been cited where appropriate in the footnotes. Among the most useful studies are: Daniel S. Lamb, "The Story of the Anthropological Society of Washington," *American Anthropologist*, N.S,. VIII (July-September, 1906), 564-579; George W. Stocking, Jr., "Franz Boas and the Founding of the American Anthropological Association," *American Anthropologist*, LXII (February, 1960), 1-17, which is excellent on the non-professional viewpoint of McGee, as is "The Scientific Reaction Against Cultural Anthropology, 1917-1920," in his *Race, Culture, and Evolution: Essays in the History of Anthropology* (New York, 1968); C. A. Browne, "Dr. Thomas Antisell and His Associates in the Founding of the Chemical Society of Washington," *Journal of the Washington Academy of Sciences*, XXVIII (May 15, 1938), 213-246, and Frank C. Kracek, "Five Hundred Meetings of the Chemical Society of Washington," *ibid.*, 209-213, are valuable for that body. The early history of the Cosmos Club is reported with devotion in, George Crossette, *Founders of the Cosmos Club of Washington, 1878: A Collection of Biographical Sketches and Likenesses of the Sixty Founders* (Washington, D. C., 1966); Thomas M. Spaulding, *The Cosmos Club on Lafayette Square* (Washington, D. C., 1949); and in the superb *Cosmos Club Bulletin* articles by the Club's late-historian, Mr. Kip Ross. Roland W. Brown, "The Geological Society of Washington," *Journal of* the *Washington Academy of Sciences*, XLIII (November, 1953), 341-344, provides a glimpse of that group; more extensive are the previously cited, Helen Nicolay, *Sixty Years of the Literary Society* (Washington, D. C., 1934), and, Thomas M. Spaulding, *The Literary Society in Peace and War* (Washington, D. C., 1947); the National Geographic Society is described in George Crossette's unpublished work, "Founders of the National Geographic Society, Washington, D. C., January, 1888," Gilbert Hovey Grosvenor, "The Romance of the Geographic," *National Geographic Magazine*, CXXIII (October, 1963), 516-585, and Gilbert Grosvenor, *The National Georgraphic Society and Its Magazine* (Washington, D. C., 1957); again, the best works on the Philosophical Society are, William H. Dall, "The Origin and Early Days of the Philosophical Society of Washington," *Journal of the Washington Academy of Sciences*, VIII (January 19, 1918), 29-34; Francois N. Frenkiel, "Origin and Early Days of the Philosophical Society of Washington," *Bulletin of the Philosophical Society of Washington*, XVI (1962), 9-24; and W. J. Humphreys, *The Philosophical Society of Washington Through a Thousand Meetings* (Washington, D. C., 1930).

Standard accounts of related institutions in post-war America are: Ralph S. Bates, *Scientific Societies in the United States* (3d. ed.; Cambridge, Mass., 1965), which places heavy emphasis on the trend toward specialization; Herman L. Fairchild, "The History of the American Association for the Advancement of Science," *Science*, N.S., LIX (April 25, 1924-May 9, 1924), 366-369, 385-390, and 410-415; this may be supplemented by F. R. Moulten, "The American Association for the Advancement of Scence: A Brief Historical Sketch," *ibid.*, CVIII (September 5, 1948), 217-218; A. Hunter Dupree, "The Founding of the National Academy of Sciences— A Reinterpretation," *Proceedings of the American Philosophical Society*, CI (October, 1957), 434-440, argues that the Civil War did not cause the birth of this institution, thereby revising the interpretation of Frederick W. True (ed.), *A History of the First Half-Century of the National Academy of Sciences, 1863-1913* (Washington, D. C., 1913); another account of the NAS is Raymund L. Zwemer, "The National Academy of Sciences and the National Research Council," *Science*, CVIII (September 3, 1948), 234-238; the importance of the Smithsonian as an agency for the development of national culture is illuminated by, George Bown Goode (ed.), *The Smithsonian Institution 1846-1896: The History of Its First Half Century* (Washington, D. C., 1897); Paul H. Oehser, *Sons of Science: The Story of the Smithsonian Institution and Its Leaders* (New York, 1949); William Jones Rhees (ed.), *The Smithsonian Institution: Documents Relative to Its Origin and History* (2 vols.; Washington, D. C. 1901); and, William J. Rhees (ed.), *The Smithsonian Institution: Journals of the Board of Regents, Reports of Committees, Statistics, Etc.* (Washington, D. C., 1879); Wilcomb E. Washburn, "The Influences of the Smithsonian Institution on Intellectual Life in Mid-Nineteenth Century Washington," *Records of the Columbia Historical Society of Washington, D. C. 1963-1965* (Washington D. C., 1966), 96-121; and Wilcomb E. Washburn, "The Museum and Joseph Henry," *Curator*, VIII (1965), 35-54.

Secondary Sources

A comprehensive survey of the literature dealing with late nineteenth century American science and culture would make this bibliography hopelessly unwieldy. The list below is therefore selective, based upon those biographies, monographs, articles, and miscellaneous works having special meaning for the Washington scene.

Unfortunately, there are few full-scale biographies of key figures in the formation of the Capital City's intellectual community, and, for the most part, it is necessary to rely on entries in Allen Johnson (ed.), *Dictionary of American Biography* (11 vols.; New York, 1957-1964); the *Biographical Memoirs* of the National Academy of Sciences (Washington, D. C., 1887-); Edward T. James, Janet Wilson James, and Paul S. Boyer (eds.), *Notable American Women, 1607-1950: Biographical Dictionary* (3 vols.; Cambridge, Mass., 1971; and obituaries in the publications of the various societies. Other biographical accounts deserving particular attention are: J. C. Levenson, *The Mind and Art of Henry Adams* (Boston 1957); and J. C. Levenson, "Henry Adams and the Art of Politics," *Southern Review.* IV (January, 1968), 50-58; H. Ludeke, *The "Democracy" of Henry Adams and Other Essays (Bern, 1950); Ernest Samuels, The Young Henry Adams* (Cambridge, Mass., 1948), *Henry Adams: The Middle Years* (Cambridge, Mass., 1958), and *Henry Adams: The Major Phase* (Cambridge, Mass., 1964); Elizabeth Stevenson, *Henry Adams, A Biography* (New York, 1956); Charles Vandersee, "The Pursuit of Culture in Adams' *"Democracy," American Quarterly.* XIX (Summer, 1967), 239-248; Dean Conrad Allard, Jr., "Spencer Fullerton Baird and the U. S. Fish Commission: A Study in the History of American Science" (unpublished Ph.D. dissertation, Department of History, George Washington University, June, 1967); William Healey Dall, *Spencer Fullerton Baird, A Biography* . . . (Philadelphia, 1915); Irving Katz, "Confidant at the Capital: William W. Corcoran's Role in Nineteenth-Century American Politics," *Historian, XXIX* (August, 1967), 546-564; Wallace E. Stengner, *Clarence Edward Dutton; An Appraisal* (Salt Lake City, Utah, n.d.); Maxine Tull Boatner, *Voice of the Deaf: A Biography of Edward Miner Gallaudet* (Washington, D. C., 1959); S. N. D. North, *Henry Gannett, President of the National Geographic Society. 1910-1914,* Washington, D. C., 1915); Abraham Flexner, *Daniel Coit Gilman, Creator of the American Type of University* (New York, 1946); Tyler Dennett, *John Hay: From Poetry to Politics* (New York, 1933); Thomas Coulson, *Joseph*

Henry, His Life and Work (Princeton, N.J., 1950); Harry Herbert Crosby, "So Deep a Trail: A Biography of Clarence King" (unpublished Ph.D. dissertation, Stanford University, 1953); Thurman Wilkins, *Clarence King: A Biography* (New York 1958); Whitney R. Cross, "W J McGee and the Idea of Conservation," *Historian,* XV (Spring, 1953), 148-162; disappointing is the portrait by his sister, Emma R. McGee, *Life of W J McGee* . . . (Farley, Ia., 1915); Charles Herbert Winnik, "The Role of Personality in the Science and the Social Attitudes of Five American Men of Science, 1876-1916" (unpublished Ph.D. dissertation, Department of History, University of Wisconsin, 1968) considers Simon Newcomb; William Culp Darrah, *Powell of the Colorado* (Princeton, N. J., 1951) and Wallace Stegner, *Beyond the Hundredth Meridian: John Wesley Powell and the Second Opening of the West* (Boston 1954), are the standard biographies in the substantial field of Powell literature; John C. Burnham, *Lester Frank Ward in American Thought* (Washington, D. C., 1956) brings a better perspective to the subject than Samuel Chugerman, *Lester F. Ward the American Aristotle: A Summary and Interpretation of His Sociology* (Durham, N. C., 1939); Lately Thomas, *Sam Ward: "King of the Lobby"* (Boston, 1965), suggests implications for Washington then and now.

The following works present important background information: Albert W. Atwood, *Gallaudet College, Its First One Hundred Years* (Lancaster, Pa., 1964); John J. Beer and W. David Lewis, "Aspects of the Professionalization of Science," *Daedalus,* XCII (Fall, 1963), 764-784; Burton J. Bledstein, "Cultivation and Custom: The Idea of Liberal Culture in Post-Civil War America" (unpublished Ph.D. dissertation, Department of History, Princeton University, 1967); Geoffrey Blodgett, *The Gentle Reformers: Massachusetts Democrats in the Cleveland Era* Cambridge, Mass., 1966); Paul F. Boller, Jr., *American Thought in Transition: The Impact of Evolutionary Naturalism, 1865-1900* (Chicago, 1969); Edward Salisbury Dana et al., *A Century of Science in America, with Special Reference to the American Journal of Science, 1818-1918* (New Haven, Conn., 1918); George H. Daniels (ed.), *Nineteenth-Century American Science: A Reappraisal* (Evanston, Ill., 1972); David Brion Davis, "Some Recent Directions in American Cultural History," *American Historical Review,* LXXIII (February, 1968), 696-707; A. Hunter Dupree, *Science in the Federal Government: A History of Policies and Activities to 1940* (Cambridge, Mass., 1957); Robert Falk, *The Victorian Mode in American Fiction, 1865-1885* (East Lansing, Mich., 1965); George M. Frederickson, *The Inner Civil War: Northern Intellectuals and the Crisis of the*

Union (New York, 1965); Mary O. Furner, "Advocacy and Objectivity: The Professionalization of Social Science, 1865-1905" (unpublished Ph.D. dissertation, Department of History, Northwestern University, 1972); John A. Garraty, *The New Commonwealth, 1877-1890* (New York, 1968); William H. Goetzmann, *Exploration and Empire: The Explorer and the Scientist in the Winning of the American West* New York, 1966); the excellent comprehensive history by Constance McLaughlin Green, *Washington: Village and Capital, 1800-1878* (Princeton, N. J., 1962), and *Washington: Capital City, 1879-1950* (Princeton, N. J., 1963); John S. Haller, *Outcasts from Evolution: Scientific Attitudes of Racial Inferiority, 1859-1900* (Urbana, Ill., 1971); Neil Harris, "The Gilded Age Revisited: Boston and the Museum Movement," *American Quarterly,* XIV (Winter, 1962). 545-566, shows the connection between new institutions and the drive for cultural improvement; Samuel P. Hays, *The Response to Industrialism: 1885-1914* (Chicago, 1957); Ari Hoogenboom, *Outlawing the Spoils: A History of the Civil Service Reform Movement, 1865-1883* (Urbana, Ill., 1961); Jerry Israel (ed.), *Building the Organizational Society: Essays on Associational Activities in Modern America* (New York, 1972); Frederic Cople Jaher (ed.), *The Age of Industrialism in America: Essays in Social Structure and Cultural Values* (New York, 1968); Howard Mumford Jones, *The Age of Energy; Varieties of American Experience, 1865-1915* (New York, 1971); Margaret Leech, *Reveille in Washington, 1860-1865* (New York, 1941); Robert H. Lowie, "Reminiscences of Anthropological Currents in American Half a Century Ago," *American Anthropologist,* LVIII (December, 1956), 995-1016, has good sketches of Washington anthropologists; Edward Lurie, "American Scholarship: A Subjective Interpretation of Nineteenth-Century Cultural History," *Essays on History and Literature,* ed. Robert H. Bremner (Columbus, Ohio, 1966); 31-80; Edward Lurie, "Science in American Thought," and "An Interpretation of Science in the Nineteenth Century and Historiography," *Journal of World History,* VIII (1965), 638-665, 681-706; Edward Lurie, "Nineteenth Century American Science: Insights From Four Manuscripts," *Rockefeller Institute Review,* II (January-February, 1964), 11-19; Thomas G. Manning, *Government in Science: The U. S. Geological Survey, 1867-1894* (Lexington, Ky., 1967); Jay Martin, *Harvests of Change: American Literature, 1865-1914* (Englewood Cliffs, N. J., 1967); George P. Merrill (ed.), *The First One Hundred Years of American Geology* (New Haven, Conn., 1942) Howard S. Miller, *Dollars for Research: Science and Its Patrons in Nineteenth-Century America* (Seattle, Wash., 1970); Gordon Milne, *The American*

Political Novel (Norman, Okla., 1966); H. Wayne Morgan, *From Hayes to McKinley: National Party Politics, 1877-1896* (Syracuse, N. Y., 1969); Nathan Reingold, "Definitions and Speculations: The Professionalization of Science in America in the Nineteenth Century" (unpublished paper prepared for the American Academy of Arts and Sciences' Conference on the History of Learned Societies in America, 1973); and Nathan Reingold, "National Aspirations and Local Purposes," *Transactions of the Kansas Academy of Science,* LXXI (Fall, 1968), 235-246; Charles E. Rosenberg, "Science, Technology, and Economic Growth: The Case of the Agricultural Experiment Station Scientist, 1875-1914," *Agricultural History,* XLV (January, 1971), 1-20; David D. Van Tassel and Michael G. Hall (eds.), *Science and Society in the United States* (Homewood, Ill., 1966); Robert H. Wiebe, *The Search for Order, 1877-1920* (New York, 1967); and Larzer Ziff, *The American 1890's: The Life and Times of a Lost Generation* (New York, 1966).

INDEX

Abbe, Cleveland, 65, 160
Adams, Charles Francis, 10
Adams, Charles Francis, Jr., 1, 3, 10, 26 n
Adams, Henry: on intellectual elite, 1; on cultural disorder, 9, 10; writes *Democracy*, 13; scientific history of 26 n; in Cosmos Club, 81, 82, 100 n; moves to Lafayette Square, 95
Adams, John, 6
Adams, Marian, 19
Agassiz, Alexander, 87
Agassiz, Louis, 5, 66, 159, 160, 161
Agriculture Department, 20, 97, 143-144, 145
Alden, James, 79
American Anthropologist: early history of, 123-127; publishes winning essays, 132; editorial policy of, 133; mentioned, 145
American Association for the Advancement of Science (AAAS): established, 57; Anthropology Section of, 117; subsidizes *American Anthropologist*, 126; and Joint Commission, 150; meets in Washington, 162; mentioned, 114, 115, 127, 131, 157
American Chemical Society, 144-145, 154
American Journal of Science and Arts ("Silliman's Journal"), 57, 94
American Medical Association, 112, 113
American Museum of Natural History, 127
American Public Health Association, 113
Andrew, Gov. John A., 160-161
Anthropological Institute of New York, Journal of the, 119
Anthropological Society of Washington (ASW): and Cosmos Club, 98; and Geological Survey, 98; founding of, 107, 114; character of, 114-117, 121, 132-133; membership of, 114, 115, 116-117; purpose of, 114; professional implications of, 115, 127-128; and Bureau of Ethnology, 115; amateur participation in, 115-117, 148; marks intermediate stage in professionalization, 118-120, 127-128; constitution and governance of, 120-121; meetings of, 121-122; papers presented to, 121-122; and promotion of anthropology, 122; publications of, 123-127; growth of, 127-128; described by McGee, 128; and Women's Anthropological Society, 128-131 *passim;* and popularization, 131;

sponsors essay contest, 131-133; and WAS, 143, 156, 157; and scientific societies, 144; popular programs of, 146-147, 159; and federation movement, 147-148, 149. *See also* Saturday Lectures *Anthropological Society of Washington, Transactions of,* 123
Arlington Hotel, 150
Army Medical Museum, 20, 62, 85, 121, 143
Army Nurse Corps, 129
Arnold, Matthew, 19
Atkins, John D. C., 89
Atkinson, Edward A., 19

Bache, Alexander Dallas, 57, 160
Bailey, Marcellus, 81
Baird, Spencer F.: and Scientific Club, 59; in Metropolitan Club, 79; on founding of Cosmos Club, 80-81; appealed to by Hayden, 93; AAAS Fellow, 114; and founding of ASW, 114; mentioned, 65
Baker, Frank, 156
Baker, Marcus, 149, 156
Baldwin, Joseph G., 7
Barlow, Joel, 68, 161. *See also* national university movement
Barnes, Gen. Joseph K., 62, 79
Bates, Newton L., 81
Baumgras, Peter, 43
Bean, Tarleton, 85
Beard, Dr. George M., 8. *See also* cultural disorder; social change, rapid
Becker, George F., 84
Bell, Alexander Graham, 62
Benet, Steven Vincent, 60
Bey, Aristarchi, 79
Billings, Dr. John Shaw: and PSW, 62; resistance to specialization, 67; and Cosmos Club, 81, 94
Biological Society of Washington (BSW): founding of, 143; popular programs of, 146-147; and unification, 147-148, 149; encourages amateurs, 148; and Saturday Lectures, 159; mentioned, 156
Biological Society of Washington, Proceedings of the, 145
Boas, Franz, 32, 118, 127, 140 n
Boggs, Charles S., 79
Bowdoin College, 32
Boyle, Esmeralda, 38
Brinton, Daniel G., 119, 127, 132

185

printed in *National Geographic Magazine*, 145; described by McGee, 146; popular programs of, 147; responds to federation movement, 149; McGee acting president of, 163; mentioned, 156, 162

National Geographic Magazine, 145-146, 163-164

National Medical College, 121

National Museum, 89, 92, 110, 131

National university movement: pre-Civil War background of, 160; during Civil War, 160-161; Henry and, 161; after Civil War, 161, 162

Naval Observatory, 20, 55, 57, 80, 97

Newberry, J. S., 87

Newcomb, Simon: deplores indifference to exact science, 55-56; and founding of PSW, 60; and consolidation of geological surveys, 87; on Cosmos Club, 94; father of Anita Newcomb McGee, 129; wins essay competition, 132; mentioned, 2, 65, 66

New York State Medical Society, 6-7

Nicolay, John George: background and public career of, 38-39; and Hay, 38; as leader of The Literary, 38-39; compared with Horatio King, 39

Norris, P. W., 114

Norton, Charles Eliot: pre-Civil War optimism of, 4; post-bellum pessimism of, 4-5, 10; helps found the *Nation*, 5; mentioned, 10, 56

Nuttal, Zelia, 140 n

Ordnance Corps, 97

Pandora, 43. *See also* Dahlgren, Madeleine Vinton

Page, Thomas Nelson, 41

Parke, John G., 79

Patent Office, 20, 59, 97

Patterson, Carlisle, 79

Peabody Museum (Museum of American Archaeology and Ethnology, Harvard) 127, 128

Peale, Titian, 59, 60

Peary, Robert E., 145

Peck, George, 81

Pierce, Benjamin, 60, 79, 160

Pennsylvania, University of, 119, 127

Permanent Commission (Navy Department), 57

Philosophical Society of Washington (PSW): stimulated Dutton, 58; origins and founding of, 58-61; immediate effect of, 60; compared with Scientific Club, 60, 63; choice of name, 60-61; membership in, 61, 69; compared with elegant circles, 61; character of meetings, 61-62; papers presented to, 62; and Smithsonian Institution, 63; advancement of science by, 63-64; compared with Royal Society of London, 64; elitist character of, 64, 148; governance of, 65; criticisms of, 65-66; establishes a Mathematical Section, 66, 67; jealousies within, 66-68; evaluated by Henry, 67; shuns specialization, 67; significance of, 68-69; financial stability of, 69; compared with Cosmos Club, 77, 82-83; and founding of Cosmos Club, 85-86; personified by Henry, 96; and unification, 147, 149, 153-157 *passim*; averse to popularization, 147-148; commitment to professionalization of, 148; and Saturday Lectures, 149, 158, 159; mentioned, 79, 94, 113, 144, 163

Philosophical Society of Washington, Bulletin of the, 63-64, 69

Piatt, Don, 10

Pierce, Franklin, 33

Popular Science Monthly, 148

Popularization. *See* science, popularization of

Potomac-Side Naturalists Club, 77-78, 79

Powell, John Wesley: and The Literary, 41; and Cosmos Club, 80, 90-91, 96; influence of, 84, 90; heads Geographical and Geological Survey of the Rocky Mountain Region, 86; and creation of the Geological Survey, 88-93 *passim*; prepares *Land of the Arid Region of the United States*, 89, prepares *Methods of Surveying the Public Domain*, 89; and National Museum, 89; and Bureau of Ethnology, 89, 116; and advancement of science, 90; reputation of, 90-91, 102-103 n, 114; seeks harmony among scientists, 92; discretion of, 93; supports Clarence King, 93; as a consolidator, 97; on Indians, 109; role in professionalization, 115; lauds Morgan, 117; as ASW president, 120; as editor of *American Anthropoligist*, 127; and Women's Anthropoligical Society, 130; and Saturday Lectures, 131, 160; and WAS, 155, 156;